"We must think of
Ramon," Julio said.

"Ramon—Ramon," Darcy repeated
bitterly. "That's all I hear! Ramon must
come first, and to hell with my
feelings. I can tuck them out of sight,
forget I have them. Play the devoted
little wife while my stomach ties itself
in knots every time I see you!"

She gazed up, stricken, at Julio.
"So—now you know, don't you," she
said weakly.

Julio's eyes were strangely tender.
"Yes, I know, *mi amada*. But Ramon
must never guess." His voice was
husky with emotion. "You have to go
through with your marriage to him.
Even if it ruins your life—and mine."

Other titles by

VIOLET WINSPEAR
IN HARLEQUIN ROMANCES

Other titles by

VIOLET WINSPEAR
IN HARLEQUIN PRESENTS

Many of these titles, and other titles in the Harlequin Romance series, are available at your local bookseller or through the Harlequin Reader Service. For a free catalogue listing all available Harlequin Presents and Harlequin Romances, send your name and address to:

HARLEQUIN READER SERVICE,
M.P.O. Box 707
Niagara Falls, N.Y. 14302
Canadian address:
Stratford, Ontario, Canada N5A 6W2
or use coupon at back of book.

VIOLET WINSPEAR

the valdez marriage

Harlequin Books

TORONTO · LONDON · NEW YORK · AMSTERDAM
SYDNEY · HAMBURG · PARIS

Harlequin Presents edition published May 1979
ISBN 0-373-70788-6

Original hardcover edition published in 1978
by Mills & Boon Limited

CHAPTER ONE

DARCY stood in the warm stillness that dazed even the cicadas and kept them silent; though the daylight was starting to fade a semi-tropical heat still smouldered in the air.

All around her the railway station was deserted and quiet; there was no one to meet her, though she had been instructed to wait for someone. Darcy waited beneath the shade of a dusty palm tree and felt a sense of fantasy creeping over her, as if none of this was quite real.

Her fingers clenched the strap of her shoulder-bag and real enough was the letter inside, its words imprinted on her mind. 'My brother Ramon wishes very much to see you again, therefore you will come to San Solito without delay. I, Julio Valdez, consider that you owe him some form of recompense for what he has suffered and I will not accept a refusal from you . . .'

Darcy drew a shaky breath. From the moment she had opened the thick envelope and noticed the slashing signature at the foot of the page she had felt almost a sense of doom. The wording and the writing were so adamant, as if Julio Valdez would come to England and force her to return to Spain with him if she dared to reply that she wasn't taking his orders with the alacrity of everyone else who knew him.

She and his brother Ramon had been students at the

Royal College of Music, where they'd formed an attachment which on her side was affectionate without being ardent. Whenever the tempestuous Latin had declared himself madly in love with her, Darcy had smiled and somehow avoided an emotional entanglement with him.

They had been out driving in her Mini car and she had been pushing his predatory hand from her knee when a van had suddenly cut in front of her vehicle and she hadn't applied her brakes swiftly enough to avoid a collision.

Ramon had been severely injured and when it became possible his family had flown him home to Spain in the hope that he would recover in familiar surroundings. The letter from Julio informed Darcy that poor Ramon was confined to a wheelchair and there was barely any hope that he would ever walk again.

It was shocking news that haunted Darcy. Ramon like that, facing a decline in the use of his entire body!

Darcy brushed a restless hand over her hair which fell into a soft natural wave above her eyes, honey-brown in contrast to her general fairness. She had wide eyebrows and brown lashes shading her honey eyes; her nose was slender and just a little haughty, and her upper lip was slightly curved in contrast to her lower one. She was attractive rather than pretty in the accepted sense. There was pride and character in her face, and the compassion which shaped her mouth had shaped her decision to come to San Solito.

She had written back to Julio Valdez that she would come as soon as possible to see Ramon. She had not added that she felt only pity for him, and that it had not been entirely her fault that he had been crippled while a passenger in her car.

Slim in a plain linen dress, with a polka-dot scarf

tied loosely at her throat, Darcy looked outwardly cool and composed. Inwardly she felt full of nerves and was very much aware of being miles from England and the few friends who knew she had come to Spain on a visit. Her mother was now a citizen of South Africa and living there with her second husband, and Darcy was so out of touch with her that it had seemed useless to write and confide the fears which Julio Valdez aroused in her. She had thought fleetingly of flying out to South Africa and avoiding this confrontation with him.

It was pity for Ramon which had tugged at her heart and brought her to Spain instead.

What was it about the letter which had unnerved her so much? Was it only in her imagination that there seemed to be a suggestion of threat in it ... an underlying hint of revenge?

Venganza, she thought nervously. The vengeance of a Latin which was said to be without mercy.

Her gaze was drawn to the sky which was deepening into flame with tinges of gold. Soon the dusk of this strange land would descend upon her, and as the pensile leaves of the palm tree gave a faint rustle she caught the sound of wheels on gravel. Her glance followed the sound and she saw a car sweeping around the corner of the station yard, scattering the silence and the dust. A man slid from behind the driving wheel and confronted her.

In the instant that Darcy saw Julio Valdez again she realised that she hadn't forgotten a detail of his appearance—dark-featured, his cheeks faintly hollowed and outlined by the sideburns that slashed downwards to his hard-looking jaw. His eyes that held hers were as tawny and startling as she remembered them, fixing her with a look that tested her nerves to their utmost limit.

'So we meet again, Miss Beaudine.' He spoke English

well, with the deep-toned accent of the Spaniard.

Darcy's throat had gone dry and she dropped her gaze to the crisp *guayabera* he wore tucked into gaberdine trousers fitted to his long powerful legs. The last time she had seen him he had been wearing a grey suit, finely pinstriped, and his haughty carriage and proud sternness had unnerved her immeasurably. Then he had made her feel like an irresponsible schoolgirl, but right now he made her conscious of herself as a woman and the feeling was even more alarming.

'*Muy buenas, señorita.*' He held out a hand to her and automatically she gave him her own, feeling at once the strong grip of his fingers and a startling tingle that ran all the way into her armpit. She almost gasped aloud, for never in her life had a handshake caused that to happen. Right away she wanted to break the contact and as if sensing this he increased the pressure of his grip, locking her hand within his, as if telling her without words that she was now in the power of the Valdez family and there was to be no escape from him.

'You have been keeping well since the accident?' he asked.

'Yes, thank you.' His strong and dominant voice was still the same, but now it seemed to play on her nerves in a more disturbing way, and when she cast a quick look at him she found his eyes intent upon her hair. How angry he had been in the hospital corridor, when he had bitterly accused her of driving her car like an empty-headed moron who shouldn't have charge of a basket on wheels. Darcy had thought he would press charges and do all he could to make her publicly guilty, but instead the Valdez family had taken Ramon home to San Solito and Darcy hadn't heard anything more of them ... until the arrival of Julio's letter.

'I wish I could say the same for Ramon, who lives

only to marry you in the chapel of the *rancho*.'

Darcy's heart felt as if it dropped into her shoes and all she could do was gape in a kind of horror at this Spaniard who deliberately informed her that she wasn't here on a mere visit to Ramon ... she was here for a more definite purpose.

It was too incredible to take in ... it was ridiculous, but she wasn't laughing.

His gaze flicked her luggage which was in a woven bag, square-shaped with hoop handles. 'You don't appear to have brought much with you,' he remarked.

'I—I shan't be staying for very long,' she gasped.

'You think not?' His eyes raked over her face, narrowed to slits of gold like those of a cougar with savage intentions. 'Well, don't worry if you don't have a dress suitable for a wedding. We have a sewing woman at the *rancho* and she can always make you one.'

'What is this?' Darcy spoke rather hoarsely, for her throat was still dry. 'I didn't come here to marry—anyone!'

'But surely you must have read between the lines of my letter, Miss Beaudine? I did write of recompense, did I not?'

'Yes, but—oh, this is absurd!' She tried to swallow and it hurt. 'Your sort aren't in favour of mixed marriages even if Ramon and I were contemplating such a thing.'

'From the time of the Moorish invasion the people of Andalusia have been forced to endure mixed marriages.' His face and his voice were saturnine. 'It may not show as much in Ramon that there is a strain of the Moor in Valdez blood, but take a good look at me, *señorita*.'

Darcy couldn't do otherwise, for he was standing within inches of her. The speckless *guayabera* showed off his dark skin and when she met his eyes she felt in him, and saw in him, the inflexible nature of an autocratic Moor. So very dark ... sensually attractive in a way so alien to her that she felt an alarming spasm deep inside her.

'You see it, eh?' The white edge of his teeth showed in an unamused smile. 'You see that I'm not to be opposed when my mind is made up.'

'But I—I have to oppose this crazy idea—this notion that I'll marry Ramon just to please you!'

'To please him is the correct way of putting it, *señorita*. He has informed me that you were lovers before the accident.'

'We were never—lovers!' Darcy looked at Julio Valdez with affronted eyes. 'Ramon had no right to tell you such a thing!'

'That is your word against my brother's, and he said quite specifically that you were his *enamorada*.'

'We were just good friends,' Darcy insisted. 'We met at the music college and attended some of the same classes. We had lodgings near each other, but we weren't having an affair. I—I'm not that sort of person, if you must know!'

Darcy tilted her chin, showing its definition and the small cleft at its base. Julio Valdez gazed down intently at her, his tawny eyes searching her face as if seeking there the telltale signs of amorous experience. Darcy knew he wouldn't find any, but all the same it left a sting to be taken for the type who indulged in the dubious activities some girls called having fun. Darcy prided herself on her self-respect, though no one could have called her a prude. She had been too enamoured of her music to have played around with any of the students, and it really wasn't fair of Ramon to have said such a thing about her.

'These days the women of Europe aren't famed for their self-restraint.' Ramon's brother spoke sardonically. 'Perhaps I misunderstood Ramon, eh? Perhaps he meant to imply that you were in love with one another but had not misbehaved.'

'You assumed it because I don't happen to be Andalusian.' Darcy told herself the man was arrogant in his looks, his manner and his attitudes. 'It's a wonder you should even suggest that I'm good enough for Ramon when you're so ready to assume I'm the free-and-easy sort.'

'I don't think I said that, *señorita*.'

'You implied it, which is just as bad. Not all English girls are shop-soiled. Some of us are still—romantic.'

'Romantic.' He raised a dark saturnine eyebrow. 'An evocative word, is it not? Believe me, Miss Beaudine, I am not so stiff-necked that I don't realise the enticements of mutual ardour. I assumed from Ramon's remarks that you had not been able to withstand your feelings for each other, and as the courting grille does not exist in your country to restrain you——'

'There would have been my pride, *señor*, or does it strike you as odd that a woman not Spanish should possess such a thing?'

There was a significant pause while the sky above seemed to spread out like a great multi-coloured fan, holding trapped in its centre the glowing ball of a sun.

The ruby fire played over the distinctive features of Julio Valdez and he seemed for interminable moments to hover like some dark eagle over Darcy, as if he might sweep her off her feet and carry her off towards that dangerous glow.

It was an absurd image, making Darcy wonder if she was light-headed from a touch of hunger and all that recent heat. Hastily she turned her gaze from his face and looked in the opposite direction, a catch to her breath as his grip tightened on her hand and sent a tingle of pain to her fingertips.

'I hope you possess courage,' he said. 'It won't be easy for you, being the wife of a crippled young man.'

'Y-you know it won't be easy for me, yet you insist that it must happen.' Darcy kept her eyes turned away from him. 'Why do you do it, *señor*? Are you so cruel and vengeful?'

'I am fond of my brother, and he seems to care for you, Miss Beaudine. This attraction has led to his present condition——'

'Oh, that isn't fair——!'

'You were driving the car and were not proficient enough to avoid the collision that took place. You had L-plates on your vehicle, will you deny it?'

'No—but——' Darcy broke off, for how could she say it, how did she put into words the fact that Ramon had been trying to fondle her when the van had driven in front of her car? Ramon had suffered enough without his family being told that his attempt to slide a hand beneath her skirt had distracted her attention for dangerous moments. She had been slapping his hand away when the van had loomed in front of them, but it would sound so cheap and nasty if she blurted this out to Julio Valdez.

'You care for my brother, don't you, *señorita*?'

Darcy flung a distracted look at Julio and her hair held sunlit gleams of amber and honey in the deep wave shading her eyes. She had to answer him, for there was threat and command in his every feature, and in the way his grip had closed vice-like on her fingers.

'Would I have come all this way if Ramon didn't matter to me?' She spoke with a touch of defiance, for he might enjoy his *venganza* all the more if he suspected that she was visiting San Solito against her every inclination. That she had set out for Spain with trepidation at her heels, and that right now the fear was crawling up her spine.

'Perhaps you sensed that I would have fetched you to Spain had you not come willingly.'

Their eyes met and clashed as the sun fell through the brilliant sky, and Darcy felt a sudden chill that made her shiver. 'Come!' The hard fingers released hers abruptly. 'Allow me to put your luggage in the car.'

He proceeded to do so, and then held open the door for her to enter. Darcy hesitated and he made an impatient movement with his hand. 'Come,' he said again, as if speaking to a reluctant child. Darcy's eyes flicked his strong foreign face as she stepped past him into the car, clenching the skirt of her dress so it wouldn't brush against him. No one had ever made her feel this cautious ... or this curious, and as she settled into the velour seat she felt a disturbance of her deepest nerves as the door clicked shut beside her.

When he joined her inside the car Darcy's awareness of him became intense. His hardness of bone under the crisp shirt, the dark tawniness of his skin, his length of leg in the gaberdine trousers—everything about him was so definite and assured, as if nothing was allowed to alter his plans once they were made.

'You don't seem to me to exhibit the signs of a girl eager to see her young man.' As he spoke he brushed his dark lashes over her face so that she almost felt them.

'I—I'm not a person to show my feelings,' she hedged, and her fingernails were grinding into her leather bag as she fought not to fling open the car door in a hysterical rush back into the station yard. How could she make this adamant man understand that she couldn't go through with the marriage he proposed?

'One used to hear of English reserve,' he swung the big car in a wide turn and within seconds the station was receding behind them. 'Of a nation good at concealing its inmost feelings, but times have surely changed in your country, Miss Beaudine. Now all we hear is that permissiveness is rife in the schools, let alone the colleges. Tell me, what musical instrument were you planning to play for a living?'

'The guitar, the same as Ramon.' Darcy spoke without warmth, for it seemed as if all her plans for a musical career were jeopardised. 'I also sing a little.'

'That is an understatement, from what Ramon has told me.' Julio Valdez flicked a sideglance at her pensive profile. 'Or does he allow his heart to rule him when he asserts that you have an enchanting way with a folk song?'

Darcy shrugged her shoulders. 'Lots of girls can sing and play the guitar, I suppose. I may not have been able to make my living as a singer when there is so much competition.' Yet even as she spoke Darcy knew that in South Africa she might have made a living as a folk singer; she had never been so ambitious that she had hoped for a recording career, but she might have landed a radio contract, especially as her mother's husband was a man with contacts, and it always helped at the start of a musical career to have someone who could give you a little push up the ladder. Darcy loved to play and sing, and she wouldn't have been too proud about accepting help from her stepfather ... her pride just wouldn't allow her to appeal to the man who sat beside her in the sleek Mercedes, making it travel at a fast pace through the gathering dusk.

He had no heart to appeal to where she was concerned. He was determined that Ramon be granted his wish to marry her, and Darcy suspected that he would carry her to the altar if he had to do so. He would force her hand into his brother's and be damned to the consequences. A *cosa de España*, she told herself. One of the ways of Spain, the arranged marriage between a man and a girl regardless of whether or not the girl's heart was madly involved.

She rested back in her seat, a little sigh escaping her before she could control it. She was being driven swiftly towards Ramon and it was like being on a carousel there was no stopping now the firm hand of Julio Valdez had set it in motion.

'You have had a long journey and must be feeling fatigued,' he said abruptly. 'At the *rancho* a bath and a dinner await you.'

'Is the *rancho* very big?' she asked, for Ramon hadn't talked a great deal about his home, being too interested in London and its distractions to ever be in the mood to discuss a place he had known all his life. He had mentioned a twin sister who was now married, but he had spoken only briefly of his demised parents, leaving her with the feeling that his brother was in control of the family estate.

At her first meeting with Julio Valdez it had come as no surprise that he ran everything relating to the ranch and its occupants.

'The Valdez property extends to many hundreds of acres,' he informed her. 'We breed horses with an Arabian strain and racing managers from many parts of Europe make use of our studs. We have also our own *bodega*, with wine made from the grapes of our *valle de viña dorada*.'

'The valley of the golden vine,' Darcy murmured, her

imagination stirred by the name despite her reluctance to ever arrive at the place. 'You appear to keep busy, *señor*.'

'Extremely so,' he agreed. 'With little time left for finding a wife of my own.'

Darcy had known he wasn't married, and it surprised her in a way. He looked the type of Spaniard who would take pride in carrying on a dynasty, and from all accounts the Valdez name was ancient and famous in Andalusia ... he had said himself that it was linked to the Moorish occupation, and it not only showed in Julio's looks that he had a dash of desert blood, it was in the relentless way he had set about arranging a marriage between Ramon and herself ... she was a mere woman and had to do as he ordered!

Darcy's gaze fell to his lean strong hands on the driving wheel, the leather strap of his watch crushing the dark hairs across the back of his wrist. She felt again that alarming spasm deep inside her, and shrank from an image of those hands holding her as they held that wheel, making her obedient to his every touch.

'It's been a long time since we had a wedding at the *rancho*,' he said. 'Ramon's sister became a bride out in Brazil.'

Darcy barely suppressed a groan as the big car swept around a bend in the upwinding road and the fading colours of the sunset streamed across the wide expanse of the sky, reflecting down on the steep shadowy hillsides.

'I—I hope Ramon is keeping fairly well?' Darcy had to make conversation or be driven crazy by her thoughts.

'I daresay he'll be all the better for seeing you.' A thread of mockery was clearly defined in the deep voice with its Latin inflections. 'He seems to cling so to his memories of his beautiful Miss Beaudine.'

'There's no need——' Darcy bit her lip. 'I'm not beautiful.'

'Not in the least.' Julio Valdez made no attempt to gallantly disagree with her. 'Your mouth is too wide and wilful and you lack the oval perfection of chin that Spanish women have. In the place of beauty you have an intensely charming appearance and I'm sure you know it. You used it to make Ramon lose his head and his heart.'

'I never set out to infatuate your brother,' Darcy protested.

'Infatuated he must have been to have gone driving with a woman who was still learning how to control a car. It's something I would never do!'

'I'm sure you wouldn't.' Darcy made no attempt to keep the snap out of her voice. 'You place too high a value on your self-importance to risk your dignity. You and Ramon aren't much alike in ways or looks—I thought so the first time we met in England.'

'So you remembered me?'

'As if I could forget you!'

'I am nine years Ramon's senior.' Julio's mouth twitched with the briefest of smiles. 'He's the Latin *señorito* who has been rather spoiled, I fear, by my aunt who is the *dueña* at the *rancho*. It was at her persuasion that I allowed him to go to England to perfect his music at your famous academy. I should have followed my own instincts and insisted that he remain at home to become my partner in the running of the estate. In future I shall hold on to my instincts and not permit a woman to persuade me against my will. If Ramon had stayed here in Spain he wouldn't have got hurt.'

'It isn't kind of you to lay all the blame of the acci-

dent on me.' Darcy felt a pain in her throat and it
would have been a relief to weep, except that she had
sworn not to in front of this heart-armoured man.

'You should have permitted Ramon to drive the car
then there might never have been an accident,' came the
curt reply.

'What a chauvinistic view!' Darcy gave him a quick
glance of antagonism. 'But I suppose living as you do
in the heart of a country with a strong Moorish influence you would regard women as mere ornaments
and chattels.'

'How I regard women is no business of yours,
señorita. You are here at San Solito in order to please
Ramon. That is your sole reason for being invited into
my home, and I advise you not to forget it for a single
moment.'

Darcy frowned and mulled over his words. Something
inherent in them was deeply disturbing to her inmost
nerves ... was he possibly implying that she might find
him more active, more virile than Ramon, whose
activity was now severely restricted by his invalidism?
Was he hinting that mutual antagonism could all too
easily turn to mutual attraction once they found themselves living beneath the same roof?

'I wasn't exactly invited into your home.' She spoke
tensely. 'And if you imagine I'm interested in your
personal view of women——'

'Women are curious about every man they meet—
and I would advise you not to clout me with that
leather bag or we'll end up having another nasty accident.'

Darcy glowered through the wide windshield—oh
yes, he knew all about women! He had sensed very
swiftly that impulse of hers to swing a blow at him with
her bag. Big, arrogant, cocksure devil!

'Men,' he drawled, 'are also curious about every woman they meet. It's the animal instinct in every one of us.'

'I think some of your instincts are cruel,' she rejoined. 'You seem to regard me as a toy that must be given to Ramon in order to keep him amused.'

'Yes, if you wish to put it that way,' he agreed. 'Be consoled by the fact that we're an affluent family and you won't be denied the things that women like. You will acquire status as a member of the Valdez family.'

'And will I acquire any love?' She had spoken the words before she could recall them, and she felt just a little appalled at opening her heart to him.

'I take it you are referring to physical love?' He spoke the words without emotion.

Darcy could only dumbly incline her head, while she felt a sudden heat across her cheekbones and was glad of the duskiness that concealed her blush from his keen eyes.

'I'm afraid, *señorita*, that you will have to suppress desires of that nature. Ramon has only the use of his upper body; the nerves that were crushed in his spine have left him severely disabled and there is no sensation for him from the waist downward. As you know, he was an ardently fit and able young man before the accident ... that he is now half useless is due to your stupidity, your liberated English ideas of women being every inch as capable as a man. There are quite a few inches and quite a number of muscles that separate the male from the female, and now I think you are up against that realisation in a way you never bargained for!'

'Oh, you're cruel!' Darcy gasped. 'You don't need a whip in order to lay it on my back, do you? You really know how to hurt a woman!'

'You hurt my brother, Miss Beaudine. You robbed him of his manhood and now he can't be lover or parent. Very little can be worse than that for the Andalusian male, believe me.'

'I—I do believe you.' She spoke unhappily. 'But you're refusing to believe that I wasn't entirely at fault when my car hit that van. I should have braked much sooner if——'

Darcy broke off. What was the use of going on with her explanation? Julio Valdez had his jaw firmly set and his adamant mind made up, and if he had his way she was going to have her love life blighted as Ramon's had been. That was the exquisitely cruel justice of his *venganza* ... she was to marry Ramon and then be denied all the natural joys of marriage.

Love in its fullest sense ... passionate involvement, of the heart and body.

There was to be none of that, if he had his way. Darcy could feel herself trembling ... Spain was a place she should have avoided like the plague, and though warned by her instincts that Julio Valdez meant trouble she had come here. It was too late ... too late to beware of pity!

CHAPTER TWO

DARCY had never seen a Spanish *rancho*, let alone lived in one, but she couldn't pretend she was looking forward to the experience. It would have made all the difference had she been a visitor, a guest who came to San Solito to enjoy herself. Instead she came under duress, and there was no pretending to herself or the man beside her that she wanted to arrive at her destination.

She sat tensely beside Ramon's brother and noticed again how sun-darkened and capable looking were his hands on the steering wheel of the dark-toned Mercedes with its grey upholstery. On the small finger of his left hand he wore a wide gold ring stamped with the same crest she had noticed at the head of his letter. He had the haughty look of authority which denoted the *hidalgo*; an air of privilege and power that was like an armour few people would dare to try and penetrate. A hard man, Darcy was convinced. If he ever shed a tear it would surely leave a stain of iron on his lean face with the well-marked bones.

Abruptly the car crested a hill that overlooked a wide valley into which the last remnants of the sun cast its flames.

'The *valle de viña dorada*,' announced Julio Valdez, and there was no mistaking the ring of pride in his deep voice. 'This is where we grow the golden grapes from which we make the Valdez wine. The valley reaches from here to the ocean and every acre of it belongs to Ramon and myself.'

Darcy caught her breath at the sheer size of the valley and she vaguely understood some of the pride and hauteur in men whose inheritance was land, to be cared for and made to yield the good things of the earth. She realised that Julio Valdez loved his land in a deep, primal way which had left Ramon less affected by such a possession. Everything else for Julio would take second place to this, and when she glanced enquiringly at him, the dying embers of the sunset outlined his profile and made every feature as distinct as if etched upon ancient bronze.

About fifteen minutes later they arrived at the *rancho*, driving in under a towering, stone-columned entrance lit by lanterns in frames of wrought-iron.

There beyond an enormous patio was a white stone Spanish residence built long ago to withstand the elements and to hold within its walls the loves and hates of those bearing the Valdez name. The air seemed alive, tinged with a muskiness that was like the memory of those desert men who had mingled their sensuous savagery with the warm passions of the south. Men who had brought into Andalusia a love of courtyards and fountains, and submissive women in veils.

The car drew to a halt in front of a massive door rampant with iron foliage, but Darcy sat where she was, unmoving even as her heart raced inside her. She didn't want to go beyond that door, too awfully aware that when it closed behind her, she would be a prisoner of a love she didn't want. Ramon's love!

Her nerves twitched when a hand closed around her arm, tightening against her flesh like a band of iron. Julio Valdez didn't speak, for without words he was telling her there was little chance of escape from the destiny which had brought her to his house.

Warm and hard were his fingers against her skin, and again there travelled into her armpit that disturbing sensation that left her tingling. Her eyes lifted to his face and searched it wildly for some sign that he might relent and not force her into a battle for her freedom. But his features were unyielding and Darcy shrank inwardly from the stern set to his mouth, the relentless look in his eyes.

'There is little enough for Ramon to enjoy,' he said. 'He might as well have you if he wants you. I have made him that promise and I refuse to break it.'

'You make your own laws—and punishments.' The words broke from her in angry despair. 'I didn't think anyone could be hard as you—please, let me talk to Ramon and try to come to some understanding. Don't treat me like a guilty person who has to accept your idea of justice. It isn't fair—it isn't right!'

'It isn't fair, Miss Beaudine, that my young brother should be bound to a wheelchair. Don't you agree that you owe him something?'

'My life?' she whispered. 'You think I owe him that?'

'If he wants it, yes.'

'It could make only you happy, *señor*.'

'You seriously believe so, *señorita*?'

Darcy couldn't stop trembling and wanted now to get out of his way as fast as possible, but he had leaned across her figure and was holding the door handle in the closed position.

'I believe you're iron all through,' she accused. 'You wouldn't care about my feelings because you regard women as being for your use—submissive to your will like those who were probably kept secluded in this house in the old days. Unlike Andalusian women I wasn't brought up to accept with sweet obedience the decrees of a man! I won't bow down readily when you raise your lash!'

'It's Ramon you will be marrying, not me.' As he spoke Darcy could feel him unbearably close to her, the hard thrust of his leg against hers and his arm flung across the bosom of her dress so she didn't dare move in case he touched her body. She ached with tension and couldn't seem to drag her eyes from his, which were half-closed as he regarded her, a smouldering tawny gleam seen through his dark lashes.

'I know the marriage won't be easy for you—or me.' His words matched the deliberateness of his gaze, and Darcy caught her breath as he raked his eyes over her, from the tumbling wave on her forehead down to the agitated rise and fall of her breast. She felt as if hot little darts were flying through her body, and something innocent in her was wrenched apart as she realised what Julio Valdez implied. He was a virile healthy man in full possession of his physical powers, and she was a young woman who was going to reside under his roof as the wife of a man who could never make love to her.

'Don't ever—ever——' Darcy struggled for breath, 'touch me!'

'Don't ever give me reason to consider myself invited to touch you,' he rejoined, with a menacing softness.

'The day will never come when I shall want that to happen!'

'What about the night?' He raised a mocking eyebrow. 'When the moonlight plays softly over the jasmine flowers, Miss Beaudine, that is when we feel the lonely need to seek a warm pair of arms and lips that answer to the sweet wrenching kisses of desire.'

'Stop it—let me out of this car!' Darcy reached out

to wrench his fingers from the door handle, but a moment before touching him she realised what she was doing and withdrew her hand as if it were singed.

'You see,' he laughed in his throat, 'it isn't going to be all that easy. Unbeknown to ourselves we react to instincts older than Adam and Eve.'

'If you think you appeal to my instincts then you're very much mistaken!' Darcy gave him what she hoped was a look of pure scorn. 'I find you tyrannical and self-important and far too fond of foisting your orders on other people. You haven't a fraction of Ramon's charm—why, I'd sooner have him as he is than anyone like you!'

'Then keep to that vow, *señorita*, if you know what's good for you.'

Darcy remained silent ... she intended to make no vows to a Valdez.

'I shall be watching constantly to make sure you keep Ramon contented—as contented as it's possible for him to be in the circumstances.'

'I can imagine the pleasure it would give you to spy on me and make my life hell!'

'You were instrumental in making Ramon's life a travesty of what it was.' The words cut into Darcy and made her flinch. 'Did you never love him? Did you accept his attentions and his kisses just for the fun of leading him on?'

'I never led your brother to suppose that we were anything more than friends. I liked him enormously. He was good-looking and his company was enjoyable——'

'He was excellent company, Miss Beaudine, but now he can't walk or ride a horse, nor can he dance the flamenco. You have effectively made half a man of him and for that you will pay, no matter what the cost to your happiness . . . yours or even mine!'

'Don't pretend it will affect your feelings or your conscience—you have none, Señor Valdez. All you have is the need to be vengeful—that would give you intense satisfaction!'

'So long as you think so, *señorita*.'

'Believe me I do!' Darcy flung back the truant hair from her stormy eyes. 'The desert is in your bones— you'd put me against a wall and stone me if you thought you could get away with it. In place of that you'd like to make me your brother's slave.'

'Come, don't be so melodramatic.' He gave an abrupt laugh. 'My brother isn't the type to enslave a woman.'

'No, but you are!' Darcy could feel a tingling urge in her fingers to let them make contact with his face, wiping that curl of a smile from his lips . . . except that instinct warned her of swift retaliation. 'You'd like to force me into giving up all my independence, all my hopes of a career in the caring of Ramon. You'd like to watch me as a cougar watches a rabbit!'

'I am certain, *señorita*, that a cougar has better things to do than to hunt rabbits.' His eyes mocked her as he released the door handle and it swung open letting in a gush of evening air laden with the scents of Spanish trees, and no doubt the jasmine he had mentioned so sensuously.

Darcy slid from the car, holding her breath as her body brushed against the arm he still held across her. The air was cool in the courtyard and she took several deep breaths as if to steady herself. She glanced around and felt as if she had been driven back into the past, into a time that had combined graciousness with a certain savagery. It was there in the high white walls and in the iron that adorned the great door of the *rancho* . . . indications that the people and possessions inside were closely guarded. A place which Darcy strove not to find fascinating ... the last thing she wanted was to fall beneath the spell of this man's house.

'Well, Miss Beaudine, what do you think of the Rancho Valdez?' Its master stood directly behind her, tall above her slender figure ... taller than Ramon and the average Latin and indicative of the fact that he was more of a throwback than his brother to those olden times when women were expected to bow down to the slightest masculine wish.

'The house seems strange to me at present.' Darcy spoke in a cool tone of voice, suppressing the slightest hint that she responded to the atmosphere of his house. 'It must be several generations old.'

'As old as some of your historic houses in England,' he agreed. 'Come, you must be in need of your dinner after that arduous journey.'

The arching door led into a pillared corridor where seats and stone containers of plants were set at intervals, the light of wall lanterns revealing a tiled floor worn silky smooth with age but still showing the arabesqued patterns. The walls inside the house weren't crusted with lime-wash but were of a pearly stone that the years had burnished, and Darcy walked with Julio Valdez into a wide hall where large carved chests were set against the walls, into which patterns in pearl and silver had been interwoven, giving them an oriental look.

Though Darcy was impressed she was determined to conceal her feelings. The man beside her was undoubtedly proud of all this and the last thing Darcy wanted was to let him see that his house made an impact upon her emotions and her imagination.

They crossed the hall which was lit by huge chandeliers and Darcy caught the sound of flamenco music

coming from one of the rooms. Underlying the beat of
the music was a kind of nostalgic sadness ... rather like
a caged heart throbbing behind bars, she thought.

'Isn't that the *petenera*?' Darcy spoke impulsively.

Julio Valdez cast her a frowning look. 'What would
you know of our music?' he demanded.

'Ramon introduced me to it, *señor*.'

'Naturally.' He said it almost softly, the dark lashes
of his eyes almost meeting across the tawny irises to
give him a menacing look. 'I have to remember, don't
I, that my brother has made you familiar with some of
our Spanish ways, though you deny that he has introduced you to our fiery passions?'

'I do deny it, but I don't see why it should trouble
you so much.' Darcy flung him a challenging look,
and for endless moments his eyes held hers almost as if
she were his prey ... which in a sense she was, much to
her chagrin. Then with a shrug of his strong shoulders
he strode to an arched door and thrust it open. He
gestured to Darcy to precede him into the room, whose
gracious proportions she couldn't help but secretly admire.

'This is the main *sala*, which adjoins the dining-
room through those iron grilled doors.' He indicated
the far end of the room where shaded lamps cast their
glow over the lacings of iron. The *sala* was furnished
with beautiful marquetry antiques, deep velvet chairs
and couches, and there was a glint of gold in the frames
of several large paintings on the walls.

Darcy's gaze was held by one of the paintings which
she felt certain was an original by a Spanish master. It
depicted a striking figure in old-fashioned armour, the
fold of a scarlet cloak concealing the gleaming breast-
plate. Darcy studied the portrait from where she stood

and felt the sudden hard beat of her pulse ... the face in the frame might have belonged to Julio Valdez.

'An ancestor of mine—they called them conquistadors.' A flame hissed and there was a sudden spurt of smoke into the room as he lit a cigarrillo. 'You notice the likeness, of course. He was one of those who went plundering for the king of Spain and did God knows what else in the name of the Golden Age. I daresay you find us two of a kind, eh?'

'We're told that what we are is what we inherit of the past,' she said in a cool voice. 'Old influences are more at work in some people than in others and I certainly agree that you could have sat for that painting.'

He gave a brief laugh and gestured with his cigarrillo at the opposite wall, towards a painting of a young woman with a rather demure air, wearing a white lace mantilla on her sleekly parted black hair. Her eyes were like black velvet and a tiny secretive smile curved her lips.

'Striking creature, is she not?' Strong smoke curled from Julio's lips. 'I have always admired a woman with lovely eyes. If a woman has those, then she has everything in my opinion.'

'Another ancestor, *señor*?' Darcy told herself she didn't want to hear what made a woman attractive to him; she didn't doubt that his preference lay in the creamy-skinned Spanish type of girl, with eyes as dark and glowing as a southern night.

'The bride of the conquistador,' he drawled, eyes narrowed against the updrifting smoke of the dark cigarrillo. 'As I told you I have not found the time to marry. My Aunt Ansonia, who runs this household, says daily that time doesn't stand still and that I should seek out a dutiful young convent girl who will supply

me with children and be as smooth as olive oil in my
life. Do you think, Miss Beaudine, that it would be a
good idea?'

'I doubt, *señor*, if the ideas and opinions of other
people cut much ice with you.' It was disturbing, none-
theless, that he should say such a thing to her. He
wanted to ruin her life by forcing her into marriage
with the crippled Ramon, and yet had the audacity to
speak of finding a dove-like bride with whom to feather
his own nest. Darcy looked him up and down and
thought him unbearably arrogant from his bench-made
casuals to his black Spanish hair.

'I am sure you have ideas about the role of women
in this emancipated era,' he said, 'and I'm equally sure
that it comes as a shock to you that men like myself
can still buy their brides from willing parents. All I
need offer is a handsome cheque and one of their innocent young daughters will be despatched to me. Though
she has never seen me she will vow in the family chapel
to love, honour and obey me. A very efficient arrangement in several ways, for it saves wear and tear on
emotions beset by the pangs of love.'

The aromatic smoke made patterns about his dark
head and he was watching Darcy with lazily slitted eyes,
waiting, she knew, for her feathers to fly at such an out-
rageous statement.

'I'm sure,' she said coldly, 'that such an arrangement
has been going on in your family for generations.
That's why it doesn't bother you to arrange your
brother's marriage to me. The big drawback is, *señor*,
that I am not from a convent and trained to accept the
absurd notion that men are my masters. I am my own
person and shall remain so, even if you compel me
to live here at the *rancho* as Ramon's wife.'

'That matter is settled, except for the actual ceremony.' His face had hardened and his eyes looked like raw gold as he bent to an ashtray and stubbed his cigarrillo. 'Ramon has been broken in body and I won't have his heart broken as well, do you hear me? You will be kind to that boy or you will answer to me!'

'Am I supposed to tremble when you make threats, Señor Valdez?'

'Make no mistake about it, Miss Beaudine, I could assuredly make you tremble.'

'I don't doubt that your brute force could frighten my flesh,' she rejoined. 'But you can't break my spirit, or stop me from disliking you more intensely than anyone I've ever met in my life.'

'It might be wiser if you felt indifferent to me, *señorita*.'

'What do you mean by that?' Her pulse gave an uncomfortable leap.

'Come, you can't be all that innocent when you were so quick to point out that you aren't a convent girl.'

'You seem to be implying that I—I find you attractive.' Darcy gave him an outraged look and felt only that he antagonised her to the depth of her being.

'I wouldn't be so immodest as to put it like that.' The look he gave her was sardonic. 'But our chemical reactions can produce unexpected results ... pain and pleasure so intermingled they can't be torn apart. Desire and disdain so in conflict that we feel as if we might go crazy if we don't find a solution that will dissolve one or the other. The simple truth is that men and women were meant to find heaven and hell in each other, and so will it be until the end of time.'

'I would think "hell" is the operative word between us,' she said freezingly.

'Hell is a warm place, *señorita*,' he drawled.

'And a devil like you would know, wouldn't he?' she

rejoined. 'Oh, it isn't fair of you to accuse me, judge me —and sentence me!'

'Lots of things aren't fair, and Ramon is living proof of it.'

'He is alive,' Darcy said at once. 'What if he'd been killed? What would have been my punishment for that, *señor*. The *garrote*?'

The horrible word seemed to hang in the air between them, while his gaze seemed fixed upon her neck, pale in contrast to the russet scarf that encircled it. He was taking a breath as if to reply when the *sala* door was thrust open to admit someone who paused dramatically on the threshold.

Darcy felt the nerves stabbing in her midriff and she sensed that she was under scrutiny by another member of the family who, like Julio Valdez, would find her guilty and hate her for Ramon's sake. It took an effort for Darcy to glance towards the figure in the doorway ... dark hair with a sheen to it framed a golden-skinned face and a pair of lustrous, almond-shaped eyes. The woman effectively posed there in a fashionable riding outfit that in no way gave her a boyish look. Her riding hat had fallen to her shoulders on its cord, and twin locks of black hair curled against her cheeks.

Abruptly her dark eyes flicked from Darcy to the tall figure of Julio. 'So this is the bride?' Her voice held a high girlish pitch that rather surprised Darcy, for it didn't quite match her air of sophistication. 'The beautiful English girl whom Ramon is longing to embrace.'

'Yes, this is the young woman.' Julio spoke abruptly and his hand gestured from one woman to the other. 'Miss Beaudine, let me introduce you to Dorina Arandoz, the daughter-in-law of my good aunt who has the supervision of my household.'

'How do you do, Señorita Arandoz.' Darcy spoke politely but didn't offer to shake hands. She sensed a different kind of antagonism in the Spanish woman; a coiled intensity of dislike that was all too apparent in the flare of her chiselled nostrils.

'Señora Arandoz, if you don't mind?'

'Oh, of course! I'm sorry for the mistake, *señora*.' Darcy felt a hollow feeling in the pit of her stomach and wondered how she was going to cope with a house-ful of hostile Spaniards. This one seemed to take it for granted that she came here expecting to be a bride ... oh God, she was beginning to feel trapped in a web deliberately woven by Julio Valdez. Without even con-sulting her he had promised her to Ramon, and he'd break her sooner than break that arrogant promise!

'In order to avoid future mistakes, I am now a widow.' A whip stirred in Dorina's hand, almost as if she felt an urge to use it on Darcy. 'My husband died a year ago of a stroke, which makes you and me a tragic pair, Miss Beaudine. My husband lies in the vault, and your husband-to-be is bound to the wheels of an invalid chair. You really must have compassion for Ramon to have come all this way in order to become a partner in a half-marriage.'

Dorina paused and slid her gaze over Darcy, de-liberately taking in the fairness that was so in contrast to her own Latin looks, not to mention Julio's vigorous darkness.

'What martyrdom!' she mocked, and there was a curious kind of insolence in the look she directed at Julio. 'Does she know that Ramon is almost as help-less as a child? Is she aware that once he is lifted into bed he's as useless as a log?'

'Be silent!' Julio gave her a forbidding look. 'That is no way to speak and you know it, Dorina. Miss Beaudine is fully aware of the sad circumstances and the extent of the physical damage to Ramon. She is prepared for that.'

'Is she really?' The dark eyes didn't look so velvety as they dwelt on Darcy's face and probably glimpsed the apprehension she couldn't altogether hide. 'You were closely acquainted with Ramon before the accident, were you not, Miss Beaudine? You know the kind of person he was, but not the kind of person he has become! You are in for a shock, I am afraid.'

Darcy was the one who was afraid and that fear crawled through her body like a drop of ice. Again she had a sudden wild urge to turn and run away from these people, back to her life in England where she had been perfectly content with her music and hadn't asked Ramon Valdez to take an interest in her. He was the one who had instigated their friendship, and that was all it had been, and it seemed beyond reason that it should lead to a marriage that would be nothing else but a bondage.

She felt trapped and wanted to escape, but dark and swift Julio Valdez would stand in her way and if she battered her fists at his hard body he would barely feel them. He was like stone, vengeful and unrelenting, and it was of him that Darcy was most afraid.

'Look at her,' Dorina taunted. 'Her face is white and she's shaking in her shoes! What did you do, Julio, drag her to the *rancho* from the station?'

'There was no need for those sort of tactics,' he rejoined, his black brows joined in a frown. 'Miss Beaudine knows her duty and is quite prepared to become Ramon's wife.'

'I wish you luck, my dear.' Dorina smiled and Darcy saw the malice in her eyes a moment before she moved her gaze to Julio and let it rove his lean hard figure.

It was a look filled with suggestion. This is a man, it seemed to say. He can hold a woman in his arms and love her, but she who marries Ramon can never know such a possession.

'We were never an easy family to know, is that not so, Julio?' Dorina reached out with her whip and slid it back and forth against his arm. 'We are all hard to handle, but you most of all, eh? Unlike Ramon you never used charm to get a woman, did you?'

'I am the last to deny it, Dorina.' He gazed down at her and it struck Darcy that they were perfect examples of Spanish breeding, both with a gleam of the raven in their hair, both temperamental and vibrantly alive, as if the hot sun of the south and its *sierras* were deep in their bones and running tempestuously in their veins. They seemed matched like figures from the same forge, and Darcy had an image of them riding across Valdez land together, mounted on a pair of his best horses.

Why, Darcy wondered, had Dorina married someone else when it seemed so obvious that Julio was the man she wanted? Was it because they were both high-mettled, the pride and passion too strong in them for the fusion of marriage to have been successful?

Darcy couldn't help but wonder if they were lovers, for it seemed impossible that those strong arms of Julio's had not gathered that slim enticing figure close against his hard bones and warm tawny skin. That her red lips had not laughed invitingly against his firm throat before seeking his remorseless mouth.

A nerve flickered at Darcy's temple and she pressed a hand there, feeling as if she might be feverish. It was unlike her to have such erotic thoughts about people and she was appalled by the level of her curiosity. Was it because they were hostile towards her, and out to punish her because they blamed her for Ramon's broken body? Was she dragging them down in her thoughts as a kind of retaliation?

Suddenly she became aware that Julio Valdez was searching her face with his eyes, the visual contact like a probe that played upon her nerves. 'You have a headache?' he demanded.

'No——'

'Then why the distrait look and the hand at the temple?'

'I'm—I'm perfectly all right, thank you.' Darcy hastily lowered her hand and resented his intrusion into her guilty thoughts about him ... his show of false concern in front of Dorina. 'You have no need to trouble yourself about me, *señor*. I'm Ramon's concern, and I'm sure we'll be able to manage our problem without your interference.'

'What a shrewish thing to say!' Dorina exclaimed. 'Julio was merely being polite and solicitous.'

'Was he?' All at once Darcy had to relieve herself of some of the tension he had caused. 'Señor Valdez has no sense of solicitude where I'm concerned and he knows it! If he had his way he'd resurrect the tortures of the *quemadero* just for my sake!'

'Is that so, Julio?' Dorina cast an impudent look at his dark face, with the sideburns that slashed down against his lean cheeks and made him look dangerously male.

'Miss Beaudine has the imagination of a schoolgirl,' he said cuttingly. 'If she really knew anything at all about the *quemadero* then she wouldn't have the stomach to mention it at all. In fact she knows very little of what goes on inside a Spaniard, which doubtless led to her becoming involved with Ramon. She probably didn't realise that Latins don't play at love; that they feel the kind of passions far too intense for her shallow emotions to comprehend. Under normal circumstances she wouldn't be marrying a Valdez at all!'

'You can place a bet on that, Señor Valdez!' Darcy gave him a blazing look. 'Your high and mighty Spanish integrity gives me a pain! All you are is a vengeful bully who finds it easy to push a woman around. Why not go after the van driver, *señor*? Why pick on me? Only because I'm a girl of twenty-two and I have no father to protect me against your sort!'

'Be quiet!' he ordered. 'You are becoming hysterical.'

'Oh, I'm sure you have a remedy for that, *señor*. You could slap me around the face, which should really give you a thrill.'

'Cold water is also a remedy,' he said icily. 'Let me warn you not to try me too far, *señorita*, or you may find that like the Spanish bull I will take only a certain amount of prodding before I breathe fire and attack. It is well known in Spain that the horn does far more damage than the dart, and that the cape is ripped to pieces before the fight is over. In symbolic terms the bull represents the male libido, and the teasing cape is the woman. Be careful that your moves are more skilful if you are going to start a *corrida* with me.'

'I should have guessed that you had been in the bull ring,' she retorted. 'You obviously have the gall for anything. Perhaps that's why Ramon wanted to go to England, because your *machismo* was too much for him to cope with.'

'It's a great pity that my brother ever went to England, for whatever purpose.' The black brows were drawn so forcibly together that their contrast with his angry tawny eyes made him look for a moment almost savagely out of control. Darcy felt a weakness in the pit

of her stomach as she realised the extent of his fury and
pain at what had happened to Ramon in her country,
in her company. It was as if Julio wanted to hook his
hands into her and shake her like a rag doll.

It came as a sharp relief when he looked at Dorina
'Perhaps you will be so good as to show Miss Beaudine
to her room?'

'Of course, Julio.' But Dorina frowned as if she
didn't much like the role of servant.

'*Gracias.*' He inclined his head and having given his
orders he strode from the *sala* and left Darcy with un-
settled nerves and Dorina's derisive eyes upon her face.

'You're afraid of him, aren't you?' She tapped her
whip against the side of a glossy boot as she regarded
Darcy. 'He has made you come to San Solito against
your will, isn't that so?'

'I came for Ramon's sake,' Darcy said defensively.
'If he needs me with him, then I had no choice.'

'You had very little choice if Julio decided that it
would make Ramon feel more of a man to have a wife.
Julio, as you realise, is some years older than his
brother and he has always been proud and fond of
him in the way of Spaniards with their siblings. Men
like Julio have a strong sense of responsibility; it is
deep in their bones and hasn't yet been eroded by the
self-interest and self-indulgence that rules men of other
lands.'

Dorina paused and drew the shaft of her whip
slowly through her fingers, almost caressingly. 'Julio
Valdez is quite a man, but it takes a real woman to
appreciate his qualities. In your shoes, my dear, I'd run
off to Buenos Aires rather than be married to half a
man.'

'If I did so, Señora Arandoz, I feel sure your cousin-
in-law would come after me.'

'In which case,' Dorina drawled, 'I should set out to seduce him.'

'I'm not that sort.' Darcy flushed at the very thought of trying to tempt Julio Valdez.

'You are a little goody-goody, is that so? If it's true then perhaps you won't mind being a wife in name only. I would find it insupportable myself, for women were made for love ... as eggs for the bacon, as grapes for the wine. All nature has a purpose and even yours, Miss Beaudine, might rebel after a while. What will you do if it happens that you can't live on duty and pity alone?'

'Tighten my belt like a Christian, I imagine.' Darcy spoke dryly, for in her present mood she couldn't even imagine what the pangs of passion might feel like.

'So you see yourself as a sort of pilgrim? Most commendable but not very exciting.' Dorina gazed as if fascinated at the portrait of the conquistador whose likeness to Julio Valdez was so apparent.

'Julio must marry if the Valdez line is not to be broken—his marriage will not be in name only!'

Dorina's reflections seemed to glisten in her eyes and moisten her red parted lips as she stood there gripping her whip ... Darcy watched her and wondered if she was hopeful of being a bride again. Did she see herself in the family chapel, at the side of the autocratic Julio as the Latin vows were spoken by the priest?

'Follow me!' Dorina spoke abruptly. 'Your luggage will have been taken upstairs to your room.'

CHAPTER THREE

THEY were halfway up the blackwood staircase when all at once Dorina paused and stood on a step above Darcy, the stairs curving like a frame around her haughty figure, smooth golden skin and high Latin cheekbones.

'Now let us understand one another.' She spoke in a voice silky with menace. 'You are no paragon of virtue where poor Ramon is concerned and I am warning you not to cast your wide eyes at Julio, not unless you want me to mark your insipid white skin with my whip!'

Darcy's heart gave an uncomfortable thud and she gripped the gleaming stair rail, the threat in Dorina's manner making her fearfully aware that it would take only a thrust of the hand to send her toppling backwards, every inch of her body striking against the hard wooden treads.

'Y-you have no right to say such a thing!' Darcy tilted her chin and was determined not to reveal her fear of being pushed, of falling and perhaps ending up like Ramon. 'I should think Don Julio made it perfectly plain how he regards me. I'd be a fool to——'

'We aren't discussing Julio's feelings, we are speaking of yours.' Dorina's nostrils flared with disdain. 'Don't try to convince me you are so virtuous and innocent that you failed to notice how dynamic he is. I have not yet met a woman who could look at Julio without wanting to surrender herself to what she see in his eyes ... the promise of an experience beyond what other men can offer.'

'I think you exaggerate,' Darcy said in a cool voice, 'but I'll not argue the point as you obviously know him so well.'

'You pretend to be indifferent,' Dorina sneered, 'but all the time you are wishing he was the one you are to marry.'

'You're crazy,' Darcy exclaimed. 'I consider him the most arrogant man I've ever met!'

'Yes, arrogant,' Dorina smiled, 'and every inch a man.'

'He's the typical *hidalgo*,' Darcy argued. 'Reared to rule others and with chauvinism in his very bones. No doubt Latin women go for his lordly attitude in a big way, but it sets my teeth on edge. He should have been around when women were no more than slaves in veils—he'd have been in his element. The man gives me a pain in the neck!'

'It had better be in the neck and not the heart.' There was a sharp edge to Dorina's voice and her body was as tensely flexed as the whip in her hand. 'Keep your big brown eyes off Julio and you and I will get along as well as can be expected. Do I make myself clear to you?'

Clear as crystal, Darcy reflected. The woman was infatuated with the Don and had obviously got it into her head that every female was panting after him. In view of the fact that he regarded herself as criminally responsible for his brother's plight, it struck Darcy as ridiculous that Dorina should be so openly jealous of her. This scene might make more sense if the Spanish woman had been in love with Ramon. As Darcy remembered him he had been charming, ebullient, ever ready with the graceful compliment.

'I have no interest in Señor Valdez,' Darcy said quietly. 'I came to San Solito for Ramon's sake, and I shall stay for his sake, if he truly wants me here.'

'You are all he talks about.' Dorina's eyes had slitted, gleaming like onyx against her golden skin. 'Darcy has hair the colour of sunshine. Darcy can play the guitar as well as any Spanish girl. Darcy is so kind and good! I have seen Julio's face turn to a mask when Ramon has eulogised about you—you, the one who robbed him of his manhood!'

Dorina proceeded upstairs ahead of Darcy, taking the left branch of the gallery which was lit by electric candles in wall holders. She walked almost to the end of the gallery before pausing in front of a door. 'This room is yours.' She threw open the door and shafts of light revealed the hulking shapes of the furniture. 'You will sleep here until you are married, and I do hope you aren't the nervous type.'

As she spoke Dorina turned to see the effect of her words on Darcy. 'The room has a strange atmosphere, as you will soon discover.'

'Most rooms are strange at first——'

'Especially those in which violence has taken place.'

'Violence?' Darcy's pulse quickened. 'Are you trying to frighten me?'

'How could I do that when the English are so brave?' Dorina gestured into the bedroom with her whip. 'Some years ago a governess of Ramon's sister died here. She took something—a man had let her down, you comprehend?'

Darcy caught her breath and Dorina smiled. 'It was hushed up, naturally, because families like this one have their pride and prefer not to have their scandals made public. It wasn't that she was pretty. From all accounts she was one of those demure women who rarely raised her eyes when spoken to. No one could understand how she ever attracted a man, but none-theless she did ... men can be flattered by coy glances and an air of pure innocence, but after a while they can find it so boring.'

Dorina paused there and held Darcy's gaze half-mockingly. 'You will want to unpack your belongings. Dinner is at eight-thirty.'

Darcy nodded and felt a sudden reluctance to enter the room where the shadows were like the dark skirts of a restless ghost. She could feel the nervous beating of her heart and her disinclination to remain at the *rancho* was growing in strength. Why should she be forced to stay in this isolated house among people who had no feeling of goodwill towards her? Surely Ramon could be made to understand that she couldn't marry him if she didn't love him?

Yet could she even say it to him, that she had come all these miles to tell him to his face that she couldn't give him even the bare fragments of love?

'My own apartment is in that direction.' Dorina gestured with her whip, where double doors gave entrance to large and grander bedrooms.

'Where is the bathroom?' Darcy enquired.

Dorina indicated a door just around the corner from Darcy's room. 'You might be fortunate enough to find the water hot, but this is a very old house and the plumbing is erratic. Julio is always saying he will have a new system put in, but he really cares more about the vines than our comforts. The irrigation system down in the valley is second to none, but he shrugs his shoulders if we have to take a lukewarm bath. He revels in cold showers himself.'

'No doubt to cool down his blood.' Darcy had spoken impulsively, from resentment of the man, and the far from idle suspicion that he might have been the man who had toyed with the lonely affections of his sister's governess.

'Yes, he has warm Spanish blood,' Dorina drawled. 'Just see to it that you don't fancy a transfusion.'

With this she walked away from Darcy, leaving her to enter the room where, alone and ashamed, a woman had swallowed a desperate remedy for love and killed herself.

Darcy sought against the wall for the light switch and when the light came on it was a relief. She glanced around before closing the door, and it was reassuring to see her hoop-handled bag standing by the stool at the foot of the bed.

A large bed with tall carved posts and a cover of heavy lace that trailed to the floor, rather worn-looking and transferred to the bedroom of a menial, matching the furniture that was no longer as grand as it had been in the old days. Darcy walked to the dressing-table, where she stood and studied herself in the mirror, as if for some sign of a change in her appearance.

She didn't know why she had the feeling she had undergone a subtle change, but it was there in her bones. Just over an hour ago she had stepped from a train on to foreign soil and as she stared at her reflection Darcy realised that she didn't wish to pinpoint the moment when she had stopped feeling like a girl and had suddenly become a woman who ached diffusely from a variety of emotional bruisings. She pressed a hand to her body and could feel the turmoil inside her; she looked into her own eyes and saw their trapped expression. She had no wish to become involved with the Valdez family, and yet her involvement was inescapable, made so by the remorseless Julio and by her own reluctance to add pain to what Ramon had already suffered.

She had grown up painfully in just one hour and would never again be the carefree music student who lived only for the harmony and magic of making music. Discord had been struck and her deepest nerves quivered with it.

Her fingers touched a crucifix of onyx and pearl that stood on the dressing-table, the head of the Virgin set into the base of the cross and surrounded by mother-of-pearl. Darcy picked it up and wondered if it had been placed in this room in an attempt to dispel its depressing atmosphere. A Catholic symbol of worship, reminding her that Latin vows were like chains that couldn't be unlocked ... yet knowing this, Julio Valdez insisted on her union with his invalid brother.

A shaky sigh escaped her, and she ached as if she had taken a physical beating. No one had ever hated her before ... no one had ever loved her desperately enough to say to a brother: 'I must have this woman ... you will see to it that she marries me.' Those would be a facsimile of the actual words, Darcy felt certain. Ramon had requested and Julio would no more deny his brother a woman than he would refuse him a glass of wine or a game of chess.

She replaced the crucifix and decided to unpack, a hesitancy in her approach to the tall wardrobe with its double doors. She drew open the doors as if the hulking piece of furniture might be hiding bones in a high-necked demure dress such as a governess might wear, but the wardrobe contained only a few hangers and a lingering aroma of lavender.

As she unpacked Darcy kept pushing a distracted hand through her hair, so that it fell in disarray about her face, the fair waves flopping into her eyes as she worked. Her fingers clenched the soft material of a slip as once again a vivid image of Julio Valdez sprang into her mind. Had he come to this room in the silence of the night and beguiled a lonely woman, his hard fingers stroking her hair out of its demure bun, his voice deepening in his throat as he whispered her name and carried her to the bed with the imps and thistles carved into its posts?

'Poor fool!' Darcy stood transfixed by what she saw in her imagination. A cold shiver ran through her and suddenly the thought of sleeping in this room was insupportable. It was haunted by that foolish governess ... she seemed to be there among the long curtains, there at the dressing-table where she drew open a drawer and took from it a little bottle which didn't hold lavender-water.

Snatching up her sponge-bag and dressing-gown, Darcy hurried from the room and entered the nearby bathroom, where she hastily closed the door. She was being over-imaginative, of course, but it was a relief to get out of that sombre bedroom.

She turned the hot water tap and hoped there would be sufficient water for her to take a bath, which might help to soothe her shaken nerves. She was in luck! The pipes shook as the hot water came through and began to fill the tub, and she felt for now a sense of security in the steamy atmosphere.

Darcy emerged with a glow to her skin, tiny tendrils of honey hair clinging to her neck. She wore her robe; the clothes she had taken off were in her hand. She turned the corner of the gallery where her room was situated ... and came to a startled halt, the breath catching in her throat.

Don Julio was standing in the open doorway of her

bedroom and when he caught sight of her, he turned fully to face her, his dark brows drawn together. 'Who said you were to sleep here?' he demanded. 'Did Dorina bring you to this room?'

'Yes——' Darcy gripped the edges of her robe, pulling them together across her bosom where her heart was beating loud enough to be heard, or so it seemed to her heightened senses.

His eyes swept her from head to toe, taking in the warm flush to her skin and the damp ends of her hair. 'She had no right to do such a thing,' he said curtly. 'You will collect your belongings and come with me, Miss Beaudine. I think a more cheerful apartment can be provided for you.'

Perversity streaked through Darcy and despite her dislike of the room she almost told him not to bother about providing another; that his reluctant goodwill was something she could do without. But before she could speak he strode impatiently into the room, passed the bed without a single glance and flung open the doors of the wardrobe. He collected her clothes into his arms. 'Get the rest,' he ordered, 'and come with me!'

He looked so grim that Darcy decided not to argue with him, and with rather shaky hands she pulled open the drawers where she had placed her underwear, scooped out the pastel-coloured garments and followed the tall striding figure along the left angle of the gallery, where he abruptly flung open a pair of doors and flicked on the lights of a large room panelled in wood with a deep reddish lustre, its articles of furniture creamy and contrasting.

'You will sleep here,' he said decisively, and dropped her dresses on to the bed with its chintz flouncing. 'You will find this apartment far less depressing than the other one.'

Darcy stared at him, her underwear clasped against her robed figure. It wasn't that he was being kind ... he was incapable of being kind to her. He knew only too well that the dark, drab bedroom at the solitary end of the gallery had been witness to the passion and despair of a woman whose downfall might lie at his feet.

'Don't stand there looking as if I'd struck you.' His voice took a mocking edge. 'Don't you prefer to sleep here?'

'Of course——' Her eyes clung to his and she noticed that his pupils were densely enlarged within the encircling irises ... something had very much disturbed him and Darcy was suddenly convinced that he had been the lover of the poor wretched governess. He had the magnetism that would draw women to him, but with equal ease he would flick them away, when they no longer amused him.

'In the mornings the sunlight comes into the rooms on this side of the gallery—you are giving me a most peculiar look, Miss Beaudine. Do you imagine I have brought you here in order to have you near at hand, so I might pay you some nocturnal visits?'

Darcy flushed uncontrollably. 'I—I was thinking that the Señora Arandoz might be annoyed that you have moved me to this apartment.'

'It isn't for her to be annoyed about anything I might do. This is my house, *señorita*, and I give the orders.'

'But you said that your aunt, the elder Señora Arandoz, has the running of the household and I don't wish to upset her in any way.'

'That my Aunt Ansonia is housekeeper doesn't alter the fact that I am the master.' He glanced about intently at the attractive furnishings of Darcy's new room, and pressed the toe of his shoe into the thick carpet. 'You should sleep soundly enough here, your dreams undisturbed by a ghost gliding out of the wardrobe.'

Darcy was startled that he should have guessed her feelings with regard to that great tomb of a wardrobe, and he quirked an eyebrow at her. 'I am not so much your senior that I've forgotten what it's like to have the fertile imagination of youth. Some of the furniture in my house is of Moorish origin; we have a chest in the library which is sealed because it contains an in-genious device, a lethal curving knife that could slice in two anyone opening the chest, doubtless for storing treasure in the old days.'

A little shiver ran through Darcy, for stamped into the features of Julio Valdez was his link with ruthless Moorish ways. He was bound to appreciate their in-genious cruelty as much as he'd delight in fountain courts and archways framing slim columns, symbolic of the erotic strain in the men who had dominated this region of Spain until driven back to the desert by El Cid and his army.

Darcy didn't need a fertile imagination in order to envisage Julio in the robes of a desert rider, eyes as tawny as sand, skin warmly dark as tanned leather, taking women with one hand and discarding them with the other.

'Beware, Miss Beaudine, you have speaking eyes!'

Hastily she lowered her lashes, as if pulling curtains across the windows of her mind where he aroused such immoderate images.

'I'm fully aware that Dorina has regaled you with the scandalous details of what went on in that other bed-room,' he drawled. 'She would do so with the mis-chievous intention of unnerving you—will you deny that you had qualms about sleeping there?'

Darcy shook her head. She had dreaded the thought of climbing into that bed where passion and betrayal had intermingled. 'Shall I be seeing Ramon later on?' she asked.

'Of course. He has to rest for a few hours each day, but he'll be joining us for dinner. You look forward to being reunited with him?'

It seemed to Darcy that he was being sardonic; he knew well enough how she felt about her meeting with Ramon, but he had no intention of letting her unhappy feelings trouble him. She felt as if every bit of her resented every arrogant inch of him, his animal grace of body and his lordly assumption that she must bow down to his commands.

'Take care, you're spilling your lingerie!' He stooped to pick up the diaphanous garment which had slipped from her grasp and Darcy caught the quizzical gleam of humour in his eyes as he stroked the filmy material. She glanced left and right in a trapped manner, suddenly too aware of being alone in a bedroom with him.

'The time must be getting on,' she said in a stifled way.

'And you wish to get dressed, eh?' The glint of humour in his eyes made Darcy realise that he could turn on a dangerous kind of charm when he so wished. She couldn't take her eyes from his face as he regarded her. She felt acutely that no aspect of her body was a secret to him and that he knew exactly how to overcome a woman's resistance. Her knees grew alarmingly weak, but if she asked him to leave her room he would assume that she thought herself in danger of an advance from him.

'Don't look so afraid,' he mocked. 'No bride of a Valdez goes to the altar without her virginity.'

'You—you're an impossibly arrogant man,' she gasped.

'Because I know what you were thinking, that I had

it in mind to toss you on to the bed and exert my *droit du seigneur*?'

'I—I was thinking no such thing——!'

'Little liar.'

'How dare you!'

'Shall I dare?' He began to move towards her with the lithe and silent grace that made him as fascinating as he was dangerous. As he drew nearer Darcy felt sure he was going to catch hold of her and her mouth went dry. She flung out a hand as if to hold him off, and he gave a laugh at the ineffectiveness of such a gesture.

'To provoke a Spaniard, *señorita*, is like waving a cape at a bull. You must learn not to give me so much opposition, and then we might learn to live in the same house without this friction between us.' He stood over her, tall and dark and sure of his power. 'You will sleep here in this apartment, you will eat at my table, and you will stop looking at me as if I have a whip up my sleeve.'

'You can bully without the use of a whip,' she retorted. 'You're in your element giving orders.'

'Am I, you silly girl?' His hand reached out and even as she backed away his fingers locked themselves about her waist and he pulled her to him with frightening ease. Darcy gave a gasp as she felt the touch of him through her robe ... her knees very nearly buckled and she hated him for his physical effect on her.

'Yes, I can do with you whatever I wish.' His eyes looked down into hers, arrantly male and mocking. 'You can struggle as much as you wish, but it won't get you anywhere but right here in my grasp.'

'You're insufferable—let me go before I scream—for Ramon!'

'You won't scream, Miss Beaudine. You are much

too British and would sooner suffer indignity in silence.'

'Is that what you relied on when you wrote that letter ordering me to come here?' Darcy could feel the warm strength of his hand right through her robe, producing in her a potent awareness of her bare skin. She wanted to resist him, but he would enjoy that. She suffered the shivers that ran up and down her spine even as her body felt as if it were burning. His dark sensual power and his air of ruthless authority were like an affront to her inner and outer sensitivity.

'I relied on your sense of duty,' he replied. 'In any case, had you not come voluntarily I should have fetched you. I have sworn to make Ramon's life as contented as possible and when he asked for you there was never any doubt that he would be denied.'

'What if I had already been married?' she asked curiously. 'Wouldn't that have stopped you in your tracks, *señor*?'

'Probably.' He shrugged his shoulders. 'But as fate decreed you were still available and free to become Ramon's wife.'

'You say it so unemotionally, *señor*, as if I'm no more than a mare to be added to your stable.'

'A palomino filly, let us say.' Abruptly he stroked the hair away from her eyes, his dark fingers fondling its fairness. 'It's to be regretted that Ramon is the way he is. There should be children running about a Spanish house.'

'They will have to be yours——' Darcy bit her lip, for somehow the remark was suggestive in a way she didn't mean it to be. Then before she could glance away his gaze had captured hers and she was startled by a look of regret in his eyes, entirely personal, Darcy felt sure, as if he were thinking of a woman with whom he would have liked to have had children.

'Yes,' he murmured, 'the Valdez line must go on, and you and I, Miss Beaudine, must do our duty by the family. For Latin people the good of the family comes before personal desires, and you will learn our ways and accept what has to be.'

He stepped away from her and glanced at his wrist-watch. 'You need your dinner and have only thirty minutes in which to dress yourself. Though we live in what must seem to you the wilds of the country we take the trouble to make our evening meal a formal occasion. Do make haste, won't you?'

'Go to the devil!' Darcy heard herself retort.

'I beg your pardon?' He gazed at her with narrowed eyes. 'Be careful the devil doesn't come after you, *señorita*. With those eyes of yours, that hair and that temper, you might appeal to the bad half of a man ... the half that wants things he is honour bound not to want. I will see you at dinner. *Adiós.*'

As he moved to the door he tossed to the bed the silky undergarment he had picked up. The door closed behind him and Darcy was left with the lingering sound of his voice and a detailed image of him that she longed to tear out of her mind. A hard emotional shiver ran through her ... the last thing she wanted was to appeal to the unsaintly side of Julio Valdez; to be shaken to the core by his sensual vigour and arrogant maleness.

Darcy wished with all her heart and soul that she could be gone from the *rancho* right now.

She longed to be gone, and yet she found herself hastily dressing for dinner downstairs in the sombre grandeur of the dining-room with the iron gates.

She chose a deep blue dress with simple lines, to which she added sheer dark-toned stockings and shoes with a T-strap. She had some Coty perfume which she applied with a light hand, and with her hair glossily combed and secured at one side by a sparkling clip she looked youthfully stylish but not in the least sophisticated.

How many members of the Valdez family resided at the *rancho*? Darcy wondered. It was a large house and from all accounts Spanish people were very conscious of their obligations to their relations, and Don Julio was obviously a successful and wealthy man.

Darcy turned away from the mirror as a look of apprehension leapt into her eyes. He made her feel unsure of herself and she didn't like the feeling. He knew how to strip her of reserve, and how to spark her temper so it matched his own. He was the most imperious man she had met in her life and he could easily make others bow down to his will. He was like a devil, she told herself tormentedly. A devil on whose altar of honour she was meant to be sacrificed alive!

The dinner gong sounded as Darcy braced herself at the head of the staircase, hating the nervous tremor in her legs as she began to descend to the hall.

Lights blazed overhead and she glimpsed a group of people in the *sala*, talking animatedly, stemmed glasses of wine in their hands. Darcy felt the racing of her pulse and she quickened her steps in accordance with the beat, reluctant to join the group and yet aware that the sooner she faced the ordeal the sooner it would be over.

In her haste, however, she miscalculated the depth of the stairs and stumbled when she reached the bottom step ... a hand reached out and caught her by the wrist and she knew instantly the strength and assurance in those fingers that steadied her.

'There is no need to run.' The deep voice was tinged

with mockery. 'There is always plenty of food for every-one.'

Darcy gave him a mortified look, aware that she would have fallen on her face if he hadn't come to the rescue. She tried to break free of his grip, but his fingers were relentless against the fine bones of her wrist, and she had to submit to the scrutiny of his eyes as they swept from her hair to her blue dress and downwards to her slim-heeled shoes.

'At least you will make a presentable member of the family,' he said.

'And do I curtsey, *señor*, when you pay a compli-ment?' Darcy resented him all through her body, for his dark distinction in his evening suit, and the impact which his nearness had on her nervous system. No man had the right to be so dominatingly male, as if every woman was his to own and order.

'Do you call that a compliment, *señorita*?' He de-liberately stroked his tawny eyes over her face. 'When a Spaniard sets out to flatter a woman he has at his command a language filled with Latin imagery and innuendo, and if I used such language to you I would expect more than a curtsey.'

'You would probably get a slap in the face,' she said defiantly. 'What game are you playing, *señor*? Are you testing my morals on your devastating ego?'

'I've already decided on your morals,' he assured her. 'I believe your skill as a driver measures up to your in-experience in other matters. I advised Ramon when he left for England to stay in the safe vicinity of the sophisticated woman, who is skilful at having fun with-out going to the extreme of breaking a young man's heart ... or his spine.'

Darcy felt the blanching of her skin and if her right hand had not been locked in his she knew she would have swung a blow at his face ... so darkly cruel it seemed, illumined by the chandeliers that were like a mass of diamonds sparkling on chains.

'You really are a devil, aren't you?' Darcy struggled to free her hand while his eyes taunted her for being so inadequate when it came to a contest of wills.

'I probably am, in contrast to elderly music masters and callow young students. I speak the brutal truth and it feels as if I'm whipping your body. There is no way for it to be otherwise.'

'Not for someone as hard as you, Señor Valdez! You get constant pleasure out of flaying me with what happened to Ramon. Don't you think I'd turn back the clock if I could and have Ramon back on his feet, full of the joys of life? I didn't deliberately crash my car and hurt him! I hate to see people hurt! I used to hide away from pain and misery in my music and I—I think that's why I loved it so much.'

'You are an escapist, *señorita*?'

'Yes, I believe I am.'

'Well, don't try escaping from the *rancho*. We are quite off the beaten track and you could stand in the hot sun for hours trying to get a lift to the station. All you would probably pick up would be sunstroke.'

'Y-you think you have me beaten, don't you?' Darcy couldn't keep a note of desperation out of her voice.

'The last thing I would want to do is beat a young woman.'

'That's a matter of opinion!'

'Yours, Miss Beaudine?'

'Yes, mine. I'm sure it wouldn't worry you to treat a woman cruelly.'

'I wonder what woman you have in mind?'

Darcy turned her head away and glanced towards the *sala*. Someone would notice this exchange in a moment and wonder what she was doing with her hand in Julio's when it was Ramon she was supposed to marry.

'Please let go of my hand,' she said. 'I don't want people to get the wrong idea—you aren't dealing with a shy governess this time.'

'What did you say?' The words came soft and swift, almost stopping the breath in her throat as she realised fully what she had said. Fear seemed to paralyse her, and then a pair of doors opened suddenly across the hall and a wheelchair was propelled into view, and the dark young man seated in it had his eyes fixed intently upon Darcy.

She met those eyes and her heart hammered. Instantly her hand was released from Julio's and she moved quickly away from him and walked on trembling legs towards Ramon.

How thin he was since last she had seen him, when his good-looking face had not been hollowed and his eyes had been vitally dark and filled with a flirtatious sparkle, an audacious daring as he chased the girls and went as far with them as they'd allow.

He seemed to Darcy to have aged ten years, a kind of hungry, seeking look in his eyes as she drew near to him. He sat there waiting for her to come to him and when she was in touching range he reached out a hand and fastened it on a fold of her blue dress. Her heart beat in her throat, for his thin hand seemed to resemble a claw and when she felt him grip her dress, possessively as a child whose favourite toy had suddenly been found after being lost, she felt a kind of revulsion sweep over her.

Pity struggled with terror. She was far from home, in the house of strangers who would see her given into the hands of an invalid without any qualms at all. It wouldn't occur to one of them to pity her ... to feel compunction that she was young and whole and entitled to youthful hopes and dreams.

'You came to me!' Ramon's eyes, deep-set in his hollowed face, seemed to pull her down into them and as if compelled she leaned down and placed her lips against his cheek. Her lips felt the feverish heat in his skin and she caught the sound of his quickened breathing.

'Yes, Ramon, I came to you.'

And, soft as velvet, came a single word from his lips. *'Gracias!'*

Such a beautiful Spanish word and it touched Darcy to the heart, mingling with her deep concern at the sad change in the Ramon Valdez she had known in London.

It was as though a dazzling light had been turned down to a glimmer and Darcy realised how hard it was going to be to say she couldn't marry him. Not tonight, of course, and maybe not tomorrow, but as carefully as possible she was going to have to be truthful with him. It was for both their sakes ... wasn't it?

She glanced at Julio Valdez as he took hold of the wheelchair and began to propel it towards the dining-room. His face was unreadable as a bronze mask, revealing no hint of his feelings, and as Darcy followed the brothers she couldn't help but contrast the tall strong figure with that of the broken one which had to be wheeled to the dinner table.

She felt a stab of pain and caught her lip between her teeth ... the pity and the uncertainty were eating at her heart.

CHAPTER FOUR

'I SHOULD have greeted you when you arrived, Miss Beaudine.' The woman looked across at Darcy and her eyes were searching beneath her swathed hair, with metallic glints of silver near the central parting. She had a Latin air of distinction and at first glance a rather cool manner, as if her many years of widowhood had left her rather passionless.

'I was called away to a woman on the estate whose child is rather sick, so do let me offer you a belated welcome. I am Don Julio's aunt, and I understand from him that you required a change of bedroom?'

'The *señor* was good enough to give me a change of room,' Darcy said at once. 'I—I didn't make any complaint about the other one.'

'I see.' Doña Ansonia toyed with a silver fork, while Darcy clenched a hand against the table edge and felt the glances of curiosity from the various people seated around the dining-table, which was long and oval and attractively set with lace and silver and stemware. Darcy had a bewildering sense of being lost in a dream. The hum of conversation came to her in waves that were distinct one moment and muffled the next. She wanted to wake up, to find herself back in London in the safe confines of her bedsitter, but the dream had become the reality and everything else was as intangible as smoke.

There at the head of the table sat Julio Valdez, and there at the side of him was Dorina Arandoz in a stylish deep-red dress, with a fan of rubies holding the elaborate coiffure which suited her oval-shaped face and yet seemed overdone for a family meal.

A manservant and a couple of maids began to serve the food, and this was the first time in Darcy's experience that she had dined in a house where the formalities were almost Forsytian. She prayed that in her nervousness she wouldn't drop vegetables all over the floor when she helped herself from the silver containers, and as she carefully placed baked potatoes and buttered sprouts on her plate she felt a pair of dark eyes watching her every movement.

'You look scared,' Ramon murmured. 'Here comes the beef, and I shall hold my breath until you have safely taken a helping.'

'It's all so formal—like dinner at the palace.' With a shaky smile Darcy speared a slice of beef whose edges were crisp while its centre was rare. She laid it on her plate and wondered how she would manage to eat it when she felt so churned up.

'You look as if you're sitting in a den of tigers.' Ramon pushed the mustard pot towards her. 'I remember how you used to like a dab of Colman's, and there is no denying that the English make certain things that can't be bettered—such as their cool-looking blondes with warm hearts.'

'You always were a flatterer, Ramon.' Darcy took a little of the mustard just to please him. 'Have you a fairly good appetite yourself?'

'So-so.' He shrugged. 'It will be all the better now you are here—I could hardly wait for you to arrive, *querida*. How fair you look to everyone else in this room. It was always your hair I found so irresistible, especially that wave which plays truant so enticingly on your forehead. I remember how it used to fall into your eyes when you played the guitar—I remember many things, *mi amada*.'

She gave him a slightly bewildered look, for he seemed to have forgotten that he had been partly responsible for what had happened that day out in the car, his hand on her leg, roaming where it had no right to be. Had he genuinely forgotten, or had he deliberately allowed his family to believe that her un-skilled driving had disabled him?

'You look at me with such wide and wondering eyes,' he said. 'Did I ever tell you they're the colour of Malaga honey?'

'Several times. The other girls at the college used to say you should have been called Don Juan.'

His smile was thoughtful as he let his thoughts roam back to his days as a handsome student of music, always in ardent pursuit of pleasure. The smile died away and his face was sombre again. 'All that is over and done with—I have persuaded Julio to arrange our marriage as soon as possible.'

Darcy gazed at him with an intake of breath. She felt as if iron fingers gripped her throat and though she wanted to cry out that she couldn't marry him, the pity he aroused in her wrung the words to silence. Soon she would have to tell him, but it would have to be in private. No happiness for either of them could come of a marriage arranged like a conspiracy and he must be made to understand how she felt.

'I couldn't seem to put into writing my own proposal of marriage, so Julio wrote to you instead and made it for me.' Ramon fingered his hollow cheek. 'Julio has the nerve for anything.'

Indeed he had! Darcy's hand climbed to her throat

where her pulse beat so madly. He had worded his
letter so she felt compelled to come to San Solito ...
Ramon believed that her arrival was an acceptance of
his proposal. There was a devilish ingenuity about it,
and the only way out for her was to show Ramon the
letter and prove there was no specific proposal of marriage contained in it. That she had come to see him as
a concerned friend and not as a fiancée.

The letter was still in her leather bag, thank good-
ness, and she flung a defiant glance along the table
to where Julio sat, her pulse giving a thud when she
found his eyes in tawny contemplation of her face.
There seemed to be a gleam of mocking comprehension
in his gaze, and she reached blindly for her wine glass,
missed the stem with her fingers and sent the bowl toppling over. Red wine spilled across the lace and pud-
dled near a silver rose bowl.

'How clumsy of you!' Doña Ansonia surveyed the
mess with appalled eyes. 'The lace will be stained—
Manuel, a cloth quickly, to mop the table!'

'My dear aunt, don't have a seizure,' Julio drawled.
'You will make Miss Beaudine feel like a criminal.'

'Isn't she already that?' his aunt snapped, casting a
hostile look in Darcy's direction. 'She is obviously a
careless creature, otherwise poor Ramon wouldn't be
as he is!'

'That is enough.' Julio's voice grew curt. 'There is
no need to spoil an excellent meal because a little wine
has been spilled. Here is Manuel to mop it up.'

The manservant proceeded to do so, while Darcy
sat there mortified. It was as if Julio had willed her to
make a fool of herself and she wanted to flee from this
room, this house, in which she felt trapped in a web.
No one here cared a rap about her, but if Ramon

wanted her, then they would see to it that he was pacified.

'Don't look so anxious,' he murmured, stroking a finger against her arm. 'Aunt Ansonia is house-proud and her bark is worse than her bite.'

It was Julio's bite that Darcy was worried about, for she was in little doubt that once he got his teeth into a person or a project he held on tenaciously, and had his way whoever got chewed up in the process. That letter of his seemed her only means of outwitting him and she resolved to let Ramon read it as soon as possible. It would at least show him that she hadn't committed herself to marriage ... all she had to offer Ramon was her sincere friendship. It was all she ever felt for him, even before the accident, when his vital, good-looking charms had been at their zenith. He just didn't appeal to her in a—a sensual way. He aroused none of the curiosity and desire a girl had to feel towards someone who was going to touch her deepest sensibilities.

'You must play and sing to us after dinner.' Ramon spoke coaxingly. 'I've very much missed your singing, *querida,* and it will give me great pleasure if you'll comply.'

'I—I haven't brought my guitar with me.' Darcy shrank from the idea of singing in front of Ramon's family and friends. 'You'll have to excuse me——'

'I accept no excuses.' Ramon gave her a possessive look. 'Everyone is eager to hear you, and the house is bound to have a few guitars lying about. Come, darling, you don't begrudge me the pleasure of your voice, do you?'

'No, but I'm tired——'

'Nonsense.' Ramon gave a soft laugh and ran his eyes

over her face. 'You look as fresh as an English flower, and you must get accustomed to having a demanding Spanish husband. That is the way we are with a wife. In Spain the man is the master—is that not so, Julio?'

Julio glanced up from his food as Ramon raised his voice. 'I'm sure Miss Beaudine realises that our ways are different from those of her own countrymen. No doubt she will learn, Ramon.'

'She was always the most adept pupil in class and our music teacher was always citing her as an example to us all.' Ramon gazed at her as if her face filled his world; as if his desire to possess her was all that filled his mind. 'She is to be my wife, Julio, so you must address her by her first name and not be so formal. I've always thought the name Darcy a trifle boyish, but as you can see, everyone, there is nothing about her which is unfeminine. I told you, did I not, that she's a charmer?'

Darcy could feel the wild turmoil of her nerves as she became the focus of attention. 'I think we should toast the bride-to-be.' It was Dorina who made the suggestion and in her gaze was her feminine awareness of what Darcy was suffering. In her eyes was a glittering enjoyment of seeing Darcy pinned to a seat of nails. 'And it should be Julio as head of the house who welcomes Ramon's *enamorada* into the bosom of the family.'

Darcy sat there in torment, wanting to cry a protest and yet compelled to hold her tongue until she'd had a chance to speak privately with Ramon. Julio's expression was merely polite as he told the manservant to fetch champagne so that everyone's glass could be filled.

'It will not be sufficiently chilled, *señor*.'

'Do not worry, Manuel, it's the thought that counts.'

'Yes, *señor*.' The man went off to fetch the champágne, and Dorina gave a slight laugh as she glanced at Julio.

'For a moment I thought you were going to dismiss the idea,' she said.

'Why should I, *carina*?' He gave her a lazy look. 'You are correct, we should offer our congratulations to the happy couple.'

The words stabbed through Darcy, for Julio knew very well that she was far from happy. She clenched her hand until the fingernails tortured her palm and prayed the day might come when she could say something that would make him writhe.

'You do look pale, Miss Beaudine.' He spoke to her directly. 'Perhaps the champagne will put some colour in your cheeks.'

'It is due to nerves.' It was his aunt who made the unexpected remark. 'Any woman will tell you, Julio, that she is nervous of marriage and I don't imagine that Miss Beaudine is an exception. Especially as she has the burden of being responsible—Ramon is the soul of patience and forgiveness, but we all know what this girl has done to him!'

'We forget the recriminations.' It was an order from Julio, not a request. 'Darcy is joining the family as Ramon's wife and it can only be hurtful to him if we refuse to be gracious to her.'

Darcy longed to inform Julio that his so-called graciousness was something she could live without, and she hoped the look she gave him was explicit. When she saw his eyebrow quirk she knew he had got the message.

'The boy is a saint,' Doña Ansonia declared. 'She deserves his whip and he gives her his love!'

'Yes, we all know that love is a peculiar emotion.' Julio spoke with such a sardonic edge to his voice that nearly everyone at the table broke into laughter.

'I think love is more exciting if it comes after the ceremony rather than before it.' Dorina brushed her gaze very slowly over Julio's face and let it rove his shoulders in the smooth dark barathea. 'There are fewer disillusions for a woman to deal with, but when a man falls madly for an angel with frosted wings he's going to be dreadfully let down the first time he finds himself with a sleepy-eyed scarecrow—which is the way we all look in the mornings, isn't it, my dears?'

Again there was laughter, except from Doña Ansonia, who regarded her daughter-in-law rather severely. 'That topic of conversation isn't in very good taste at the dining-table,' she reproved. 'You carry your airs of sophistication just a little too far, Dorina.'

'I'm not so very sophisticated,' Dorina drawled. 'I think I have a strong dash of the Moorish harem in me. I rather like the idea of being dominated and made to react entirely like a woman. I can think of nothing more exciting than being carried off by a man and made to give in to his every wish and whim.'

'You read too many inflammable novels,' her mother-in-law snapped. 'I have seen those parcels of books arriving from England and I know you lie in bed for hours reading them. You will strain your eyes.'

'And no doubt my imagination.' Dorina gave that kittenish giggle that came so oddly from her scarlet lips. 'The books are amusing and I must admit that some of them are quite daring. They assist my English —don't you agree, Miss Beaudine, that I speak excellent English? My every word can be understood, don't you think?'

'Yes, *señora*, there is no mistaking the meaning in your words.'

'*Gracias*.' Dorina slid her gaze to Ramon. 'If English girls are like those depicted in the novels, then you had better be on your guard, *caro*. It is truly amazing the desires that burn beneath their cool blonde exteriors.'

'Darcy isn't like that,' Ramon rejoined. 'Keep your pretty claws to yourself, Dorina.'

'Are you threatening to clip them?' she asked sweetly.

'I'll run over them if you don't watch out.'

'Stop squabbling, you two.' Julio said it lazily, but his eyes were narrowed and alert. 'There will be no more talk of what goes on in promiscuous novels——'

'Why not, Julio?' she asked, lowering her dusky lashes and then lifting them as if she and Julio were alone and she was intent on seducing him. 'It's all part of life and each one of us is capable of being promiscuous if the occasion is attuned to it and our feelings carry us away. Deny it if you dare, *querido*.'

'I rarely deny the truth,' he replied. 'We're all fallible and life is made exciting by the incredible fact that we are magnetically held to a great spinning ball in the sky and each of us is capable of falling from grace. Hence the fascination of Lucifer. He's real to us because he's sinner and saint, as we all are.'

'Oh, Julio——' Her red lips stayed apart and her eyes were fixed darkly on his face. She breathed quickly as if her pulse was racing, the red silk clinging to the rise and fall of her breast. In that moment it was obvious that Dorina Arandoz had little defence against Julio Valdez, and Darcy had to look away from the Spanish girl. It was as if she offered herself ... as if like Salome she would rise and dance for the tyrant Herod, who would let her have whoever's head she asked for.

Darcy gave a shiver ... the image was almost barbarously real, as if she'd had a glimpse of Spanish passion.

The tension relaxed as Manuel came into the room carrying a large bottle of champagne wrapped in a snowy napkin. Each wine glass was carefully filled and Julio rose to his feet, tall at the head of the table, his tawny eyes shifting from his brother Ramon to Darcy's tense face. *No*, she cried out dumbly. *Don't do this to me!*

Ignoring the plea he must have seen in her eyes, Julio raised his glass, the bowl and stem looking delicate in his strong hand. 'We Andalusians know what an important and symbolic occasion it is when a man and a young woman declare their intention to marry.' He spoke with a deliberation that held Darcy almost in shock. 'My brother Ramon, whose welfare I hold close to my heart, has declared his intention of taking an English girl for his bride, and so I ask of you all to drink to the happiness of their future union.'

He didn't falter on the word that was meant to imply the uniting of two hearts that shared an irresistible love, the fusion of two bodies in that act of love.

He calmly tipped his champagne between his lips, knowing what a travesty of a union it would be and yet forging the chains and twisting the keys that would lock her up with Ramon. *I hate you ... hate you ...* so cried her heart while her lips were pressed coldly to the rim of her wine glass. She felt the flow of the wine through her veins, but nothing warmed her body. She managed to smile at the congratulations and tried not to let it show that Ramon's grip on her hand felt like a shackle.

'You have the bracelet, Julio?'

Ramon's brother at once pushed back his chair and came striding to the wheelchair. He took a velvet jewel-case from his pocket and silently handed it to Ramon, who clicked it open and displayed the sudden dazzle of diamonds. He withdrew the bracelet and played with it in his fingers.

'We give rings to each other only at the ceremony,' he told Darcy. 'You like this, eh?'

She gazed at the band of gems as if it were a snake he was about to twine about her arm, then in a silent agony that wouldn't be contained she flung a look at Julio, her eyes silently begging him not to let the torture go any further.

Julio gazed down at her for what seemed an endless moment, then he swung on his heel and returned to his place at the table, where he took hold of his wine and tipped it down his throat.

'Your arm, *querida*.' Ramon spoke firmly and Darcy obeyed him like an automaton ... there seemed at this precise moment little else she could do. His fingers clasped the bracelet about her flesh, and then he took hold of her hand and carried it to his lips, burying them in her palm in front of everyone.

'Diamonds suit your skin,' he murmured. 'Andalusian women look better in pearls.'

'The bracelet is very nice.' Darcy had to say something, for everyone was looking at her. 'Th-thank you, Ramon.'

'She will make a charming bride, eh?' He glanced around the table looking proud. 'In the mantilla of white lace Darcy will look angelic and I'll be the envy of every man at the wedding—though no doubt the women will be of the opinion that she isn't getting a very good bargain in return. Isn't that so, Dorina?'

Dorina blinked her dark lashes at him and fingered the teardrop pearl that hung against the bosom of her dress. 'As if I would think anything so cruel, Ramon! I consider Miss Beaudine to be a lucky girl to be marrying one of the heirs of the Valdez estate. She would need to work for her living were it otherwise, eh?'

'I—I wouldn't marry any man for his money,' Darcy said indignantly.

'You mean that you have to be madly in love with him?' Dorina stared deliberately at Darcy. 'How very romantic of you, when we were all beginning to think that the English had lost their romantic natures and had become hedonists. All the same, it's nice to have money. It provides such nice feathers for the nest, not to mention diamonds. Didn't the writer Anita Loos say that diamonds are a girl's best friend?'

'She also said that gentlemen prefer blondes.' It was Julio who spoke, his tawny eyes narrowed as they dwelt on Dorina's face. 'We are all aware that there are no mercenary reasons attached to Ramon's engagement, so use those charming lips, *carina*, to eat your dessert.'

'I am at your command, Julio.' Her dark eyes smiled into his as she took her fork and slowly raised hot cherry tart to her mouth, opening it and sliding in the fruit in a sensuous manner.

Darcy dragged her gaze from the scene and looked down at her own plate of steaming dark cherries in pastry and thick cream. Normally she was a girl with a good appetite, but tonight she was having to force down each mouthful. At any other time she would have found the dessert delicious, but right now the aroma of the cherries in cream was making her feel squeamish.

She couldn't be made to marry against her will, she told herself. The days of enforced marriage were surely over and she'd tell Ramon—and that arrogant brother of his! She'd make it plain to both of them——

'Tonight you eat like a bird.'

She glanced at Ramon, who had become almost a stranger, someone she could hardly associate with the carefree young Latin she had known at the college. 'I don't seem to have much appetite,' she replied.

'I can remember when you could eat steak and chips with the appetite of a young stevedore.' Ramon's eyes were wistful as he looked at her. 'There was so much to enjoy in those days, now for me there is so very little. That's why I'm so happy you have come to me.'

Darcy gazed at him stricken. He had been intensely alive, from the dark crown of his head to his restless feet that could move so adroitly to the rhythm of the flamenco music. Now he couldn't move his legs, nor sway his body to the music of Andalusia. Now he couldn't pursue a woman and had to ask his brother to do it for him.

Darcy closed her eyes tightly and tried not to remember the screeching of car wheels on tarmac, the shattering of glass, the thud of Ramon's body as he was partly hurled through the torn side of the Mini where the van had driven into them.

The ambulance had rushed them to hospital, where Darcy was found to be suffering from bruising and concussion. Upon her recovery she had tried to see Ramon and had been thwarted by his family, who had forbidden the nurses to let her into his sickroom. It was Julio Valdez whom she had seen, who in no uncertain terms had let her know what he thought of her. Then as now he had refused to be convinced that she had not been entirely at fault. He had to find a scapegoat, and she was it!

She rested her fork and dessert spoon, knowing she would gag if she tried to eat any more. A cold sort of bleakness had her in its grip. That diffused sense of pain made her feel almost as bruised as at the time of the accident. She hadn't been allowed to see Ramon, and had come to Spain in order to assure herself that he was quite well. She hadn't dreamed that Julio had deliberately set a trap for her, from which she could only escape by hurting Ramon's pride and the love he felt for her.

She would never forgive Julio for what he had done. A shrewd and experienced judge of women, he had judged her that time in England and felt confident that she could be forced into giving up her personal hopes and dreams in marriage to a man other young women might regard as a burden.

Darcy felt desperately sorry for Ramon, but she just had to find the courage to show him Julio's letter. Once he realised that she had come to San Solito as a friend and nothing more, then he would do the gallant thing and release her from a promise she had never really made. He would realise as she did that they stood not a chance of being happy if she married him because Julio played on her pity, and the sense of guilt even the most blameless driver feels when someone is hurt by the vehicle they're in control of.

'Come, we will go to the *sala*.' Doña Ansonia rose to her feet, a rather angular figure in black figured lace. 'When you men are ready, we shall ask Ramon's young woman to sing for us. He has said often enough that she has a pleasant voice.'

'A rare and charming one, *tía cara*,' he smiled.

'I—I'd really like to be excused,' Darcy broke in, a hand pressed to the nervously beating pulse in her throat. 'I don't feel like singing——'

'Nonsense!' Doña Ansonia gave her a haughty look. 'A cup of coffee will wake you up and you will sing for Ramon as he wishes.' His aunt swept a ringed hand towards him, indicating his wheelchair, implying without words that he had little enough to give him pleasure. 'I hope you aren't one of those young women who have moods and headaches at the slightest whim. It

really won't do if you're going to become a member
of the Valdez family.'

Darcy ached to reply that her very last wish was to
take the name of Valdez ... she wanted to shout it, but
instead a helpless feeling swept over her, as of a fly in
a web. The more she struggled the deeper enmeshed she
seemed to become, and when Doña Ansonia took her
firmly by the arm she walked meekly into the *sala*,
docile as a prisoner who feared her jailors.

'You will sit beside me.' A velvet couch was indicated
and Darcy sat down, aware of the other women taking
chairs, and of Dorina draping herself elegantly against
the black grand piano where she opened a gold case
and took from it a slim cheroot. Her lighter snapped
and shot a flame at the tip of the cheroot and as she
released smoke from her nostrils she was watching
Darcy and letting it show in her eyes that she was enjoying the situation. She obviously sensed that Darcy was
holding on to her composure by her fingertips and was
waiting to see how long Darcy could endure the tension
without a cry for help.

Coffee and cognac were being served when the men
strolled into the *sala*, and Darcy noticed at once that
one of them was carrying a guitar, a honey-coloured
instrument with silk ribbons hanging from it.

'Ah, that instrument used to be played by Raquel,
my nephew Ramon's twin sister who married and lives
in Brazil.' Doña Ansonia beckoned to the young man
who carried it. 'Carlos, bring the guitar over here.
Ramon's young woman is going to play and sing for us;
she has been telling me about the college where she was
a pupil of music.'

The good-looking young Spaniard brought the
instrument to Darcy and she felt the flick of his eyes

over her hair and face as he handed it to her. 'Don Julio had it brought down, *señorita*. I believe it has been kept tuned.'

The feel of a guitar was familiar and somehow re-assuring and Darcy placed it in position and ran her fingers, over the six strings, which sang out sweetly, melodiously, with a deep honey tone. She realised at once that the guitar had been made in Spain and was perfectly balanced, and feeling Carlos still watching her, she returned his look, but very briefly. Ramon had been wheeled into the room and instinct warned her that he'd be jealous if he saw her looking at a young man who was upright, able, somehow like Ramon had been before the accident.

As her fingers ran light and questing over the guitar strings so her thoughts ran with them. The last time she had played for Ramon he had stood at her side like Carlos, his dark eyes intent upon her, every line and sinew of his body as vibrant with life as the Spanish music. Oh God, would she find the courage to hurt him all over again? Would it not be better if she took the coward's way and left San Solito without chancing a confrontation with him?

'Play *Cielito lindo, mi amada.*' It was Ramon who spoke and Darcy hoped the shiver his words induced wasn't detected by Doña Ansonia. 'We all long, don't we, for a little heaven?'

There was a little laughter, and for some reason Darcy's glance was drawn to the proud, strong face of the man who stood a few paces behind Ramon's chair. He was somehow in the shadows, out of range of the shaded lamps, but Darcy could see the glint of his eyes, intent, watchful, aware of her lack of love for his brother yet resolved to bring about their joyless union.

Again a slight shiver ran through Darcy as she began

to play the music, the guitar ribbons gay and bright against her blue dress, her instinctive skill as a musician picking up the emotion she was feeling and transmitting it to her performance. Darcy sensed at once that she was playing very well, as if she struck chords unaroused in her before she came to this house. The Spanish atmosphere was suited to the music, yet it was ironical that she played so heavenly when she was feeling so low. It had to be the instrument, she told herself, for it was certainly superior to the one she owned, which lay in its case among her other belongings in her faraway London lodgings.

Quietly, dreamily she completed the music and at once there were murmurs of '*Otra vez!*' and a spontaneous burst of applause. Genuine applause, for Spaniards were critical of guitar playing, their regard for the instrument being highly personal.

Darcy flushed and felt a momentary pleasure that was washed away as soon as she caught sight of Ramon, whose hands were gripping the arms of his wheelchair, the knuckles as white as polished bone. He was remembering London, she knew it right away. Recalling those evenings when the students had got together and given impromptu concerts, crowded together in someone's bedsitter, drinking wine, eating sausage, laughing and young and full of the future.

A fist seemed to grab at Darcy's heart. It was all over for Ramon, the gaiety and the ardent expectations, and if he was embittered could anyone really blame him?

Her fingers gripped the guitar ribbons ... if he had convinced himself of her guilt then he must wish her harm in return, and a man as shrewd as Julio Valdez must be aware of what really lay in Ramon's heart. She flung a look in Julio's direction, but he had moved into the orbit of Dorina and they stood together near the

piano. She was smiling up at him, as if inviting him to
crush her dark red lips, and they seemed so right together that it was like looking at one of those Regency
paintings of a couple lost in each other's eyes.

Even as Darcy admired their physical blending, she
wondered how he could be so heartless when he looked
so powerfully protective in conjunction to a woman.
Everything about him threw into relief the femininity
of the female figure; his shoulders loomed strong and
sure, his hands could span a slim waist, and in his
features power and passion seemed equally measured,
the one controlling the other so he would never be
mastered by his power, nor at the mercy of the passion
someone might arouse in him.

Strong, in command, a man a woman might turn to
in need, yet Darcy had to face the fact that where she
was concerned Julio Valdez was without mercy.

A sigh shook her, and she gave Carlos a bewildered
look when he leaned down to her and asked her to
sing.

'I—I know only English songs,' she said evasively.
'You probably prefer something Andalusian——'

'Not at all, señorita.' His smile reminded her of the
old Ramon and she realised that he must be a cousin.
'A charming English girl should sing of the things she
understands—and loves. It isn't wise to go against what
is in our hearts; to do so is like trying to grow carna-
tions in a garden of stones.'

Darcy stared up at him, rather fascinated. 'You
speak like a man who loves gardens,' she said.

'So I should, señorita, when I work for Don Julio in
the *valle de viña dorada*. I am Carlos Montoyos and I
am the valley foreman.'

'I am pleased to know you.' Darcy smiled, and for the
first time this evening her lips didn't have to be forced

into smiling. 'What would you like me to sing, *señor*?'

'Something you are fond of,' he replied. 'Something you liked when you were a small girl without the cares of a grown woman.'

His words touched off a memory and she smiled a little ... she and her father in their Braintree garden, so long and winding and packed with cabbages, onions, potatoes and rhubarb. He had loved gardening and the pair of lilac trees edging the irregular lawn where her swing was hung.

Softly, lost in her memory, Darcy began to play and sing *We'll Gather Lilacs*, the evocative and lovely Ivor Novello song her father had so often whistled to himself as he dug his garden or enjoyed a pipe of tobacco and a book beneath one of the lilac trees. He had been much loved by Darcy, who had been too young to know that he had bone-marrow disease and was bound to die.

Tears stood in her eyes and suddenly she could no longer bear to sing, or to stay in this room among strangers who thought of her as the girl who had crippled Ramon.

Darcy jumped to her feet and flung down the guitar on the velvet couch. She fled, snatching at the skirt of her dress, the tears breaking loose from her eyes and falling to her cheeks. Someone cried her name ... she knew it was Ramon, but she didn't falter, heading for the staircase that led upwards to the shadowy gallery, to the room where she could shut the door, turn the key and keep at bay the Valdez brothers.

Ramon couldn't follow her physically, but Julio could, and she quickened her speed as if the devil himself were at her heels.

CHAPTER FIVE

DARCY was panting as she stood with her shoulders pressed to the hastily closed doors of her bedroom, her fingers still gripping the handle with the empty keyhole. There was no key to turn! She was unable to lock herself in and feel safe from Julio Valdez!

She glanced about in a hunted fashion, saw her leather shoulder-bag standing on the stool at the foot of the bed and knew a compulsion to remove his letter and have it on her person when the moment came to show it to Ramon. It would release her from an impossible situation ... it had to.

Her hands shook as she flung back the flap of the bag and fumbled about inside, seeking the thick envelope which contained the letter. She couldn't find it! In a kind of desperation she emptied the contents of the bag on to the bed ... everything was there except the envelope with the firm, slashing writing on the front of it.

Darcy stared at the little mound of belongings in the centre of the bedcover ... the letter had definitely been in her bag, and now it had vanished. Slowly she glanced around the room which Julio had chosen for her, removing her from the sombre one at the other end of the gallery. He had been standing in that other room when she had come from the bathroom; he could so easily have opened her bag and removed the letter

78

which Ramon believed to contain his proposal of marriage.

Certainty struck at Darcy ... that was what Julio had done. He had anticipated her and removed the evidence which would have convinced Ramon that she hadn't come to San Solito with the intention of becoming his wife.

She started to pace back and forth in a fury of annoyance. How dared he do such a thing! How dared he even touch her bag, let alone remove something that was her property! She wanted to tell him what she thought of him, yet on the other hand she never wanted to see him again. He was arrogant and conniving and capable of base behaviour in achieving his own way. He obviously believed that without the letter she wouldn't find the nerve to confront Ramon ...

Darcy came to a halt and gripped hold of a bedpost as if she needed its support. He was right! She couldn't bear the thought of telling Ramon to his face that she couldn't marry him, no matter if it was love or hate that made him want her. The diamond bracelet glimmered on her arm, an acute reminder that he believed himself engaged to her in the Latin tradition. The gems held a sharp brilliance as of sparkling ice with a burning shimmer at the centre of each stone. Expensive and beautiful, but nonetheless a shackle.

She couldn't seem to drag her gaze from the diamonds and was standing there, one hand still gripping the bedpost, when the doors were flung open to admit someone, who just as quickly closed them behind him.

Darcy dragged her gaze from the bracelet and for several moments she saw Julio Valdez as if through a haze.

'I have come on behalf of Ramon,' he said curtly. 'He was concerned at the abrupt way you left the *sala*. He felt certain you must be feeling unwell.'

'I'm furious,' she flung at Julio. 'You've ransacked my bag and taken the letter you wrote to me. You made out to Ramon that you proposed on his behalf, but you know that isn't true. You know I didn't come here with the intention of marrying him!'

'I know it, but he doesn't—and he isn't going to know.' Julio moved away from the doors and began to cross the room towards her. He looked taller still in his dark suit, and there seemed to be threat in the set of his shoulders and in the tawny gleam of his eyes. He walked silently like some creature of the night.

'You took that letter,' she accused, 'so don't bother to deny it!'

'I've no intention of doing so.' He loomed above her and there was no mistaking the threat in every line and bone of him; there was also a savage aliveness in his eyes looking down into hers. 'If I had written that proposal of marriage to you, I am fully aware that you'd have run off rather than marry an invalid. Will you deny that?'

There was no denying it and her eyes spoke for her. Had she loved Ramon it would have been a different matter, but she had never loved him in the way that made sacrifice almost a joy so long as it was made on behalf of someone adored.

'You see,' he taunted. 'I relied instead on your sense of British fair play to bring you to Spain, and it worked, didn't it?'

'You're as clever as the devil, aren't you?' Darcy glared up into his dark face that was so hatefully fascinating. 'Oh, how can you expect me to give up everything, my career, my own way of life? You haven't the right——'

'Don't speak to me of rights!' He bared his teeth on the word. 'Ramon had the right to be strong and able, and then you might have been only too ready to fall into his arms. Only a month ago he took a gun of mine and he'd be dead right now if I hadn't walked into the tack room just as he put the gun to his head. I wrenched the weapon away from him, and I wrenched out of him if there was anything—anyone at all who could make his life feel worthwhile.'

Julio paused and made a savage gesture towards Darcy. 'You! Ramon said if he could have you—that you were the one girl he couldn't get out of his mind. You, who we kept from seeing him at the time of the accident, assuming his ordeal had been sufficient without bringing to his bedside the one who had laid him on his back. Well, Miss Beaudine, if my brother wanted you, then he was damn well going to have you—any way, by whatever means it took. I thought of brute force —of coming in person to fetch you to him, but Ramon seemed to think you had a certain sensitivity, so I decided to be subtle. It paid off in aces, wouldn't you agree?'

Darcy could only look at him and wonder why fate had been so perverse that sunny, seemingly carefree day when the English daffodils were out in bloom, taking and breaking a young man who had harmed no one in his life, and placing her in this invidious situation. Stark in her mind was an image of Ramon with a gun at his head, Julio's swift hand reaching out to seize it a moment before the trigger was pulled.

'Oh God——' The words came chokingly from her. 'Is it true—did Ramon try to kill himself?'

'Of course it's true. He meant to die because he couldn't face an empty future. He broke down in tears and said that no woman would want him—the way he is. He said that before the accident he planned to marry you——'

'No,' Darcy shook her head, 'we never talked seriously of anything like that. We were young and out to enjoy ourselves, and I wasn't the only girl he went out with. You must believe me!'

'Perhaps I do.' He shrugged his shoulders. 'I'm fully aware that Ramon liked the girls, and why not? He was attractive to them, and they were attracted to him. Even the way he is now, he isn't a man to live alone without a woman, and tonight, Miss Beaudine, you permitted his bracelet to be clasped about your arm. You knew what it signified——'

'Yes,' she agreed, 'but I couldn't refuse him at the dinner table, with everyone looking on. Th-that would have been too cruel——'

'You were waiting, eh? You were going to show him my letter and prove to him that no proposal of marriage had been made on his behalf. I said earlier on that you have speaking eyes——'

'And you have the mind of a devil!' she flung at him. 'Conniving and contorted, seeing all the angles and making sure you have your way no matter whose feelings get mauled in the process.'

'You do appear to have a natural talent for exaggeration,' he drawled. 'As Dorina pointed out, as Ramon's wife you'll have a softly feathered bed and a few more diamonds to deck that fair skin of yours. You will want for nothing——'

Upon that word he abruptly paused and his eyes swept over her. His dark brows drew together and his sideburns seemed even more distinct and slashing, following the hard bone structure of his face. 'In a material sense,' he added. 'It isn't as if you have to live in rooms and take in washing, is it?'

'I hate you,' Darcy said, with a quiet intensity. 'I'm going to tell Ramon exactly what you've done—even if I haven't the letter to show him, he'll believe me.'

'No doubt he will,' Julio agreed. 'And the very next time he gets hold of a gun I am certain he'll use it if there's no one around to foil him. Do you want that to happen? Will it ease your conscience if Ramon dies by his own hand, having been driven halfway there by you?'

'Cruel—you're so cruel!' Darcy suddenly flung herself down on the bed and buried her face in the cover, writhing in a torment she couldn't control.

Hands gripped her shoulders, hard, warm, relentlessly pulling her upright and giving her a shake. 'Don't be a child! You went around with my brother and made him care for you. The consequences aren't so very terrible, are they?'

Darcy wished she could have said no, but when Julio touched her, and no matter how much she despised his trickery, when his hands came in contact with her body it was as if all the cells and nerves and finest bones of her being responded to his maleness.

She was deeply shocked by her own response, but she couldn't ignore it ... she went strangely boneless and it was a frightening, primitive, unholy reaction. It was as if something bad in her was reaching out for the devil in him.

He stared down at her, at her hair flung half across her eyes, the décolleté of her dress dragged to one side by his grip on her. His face was lean, hard, the cheeks indrawn, and her pulse beat heavily during the silence that hung between them.

She saw it in his eyes, and felt it in her heart, that the consequences could be volcanic if she married Ramon and lived under the same roof as Julio Valdez. Something savage in him appealed to the sensuality in her ... that which her music and her sensitivity had concealed until this moment in a Spanish bedroom, his warm dark hands pressing into her flesh.

'Let me go,' she whispered. 'I told you not to touch me!'

He flung her away from him so she fell back heavily on to the bedcover, her hair flung out golden against the creamy lace, her body slimly curved in the blue silk dress, Ramon's diamonds dazzling against her skin. Julio stared down at her with narrowed eyes seething with a mixture of feelings.

'I could strangle you,' he half-groaned.

'Go ahead,' she said. 'It'll be quicker that way.'

'You have to marry Ramon—you know it, don't you?'

'I know only what you tell me, Julio.' Suddenly a taunting little smile crept into her eyes, for the woman he had aroused was telling her how to torment him. 'I shan't suffer alone, shall I? Now there'll be two of us wearing the hair shirt in the one house, you and I, brother-in-law. How are you going to like the feel of that against your tawny skin? You'll always know it's there, men being the way they are.'

'I knew it,' his teeth gritted, white and hard. 'I knew when I met you in England. Maybe you came to Spain because of me—did you?'

Her fingernails clawed at the bedcover, and then, unable to control her fury, she reared up and went for his eyes. But he was quick as a wild animal and she was gripped, hauled against him, her cry of denial locked between his lips as he kissed her bruisingly, forcing her down beneath him until not an inch of her was unaware of his lean and powerful body. She thrashed about in her effort to be free of him, but it was like being caught in the merciless grip of an undertow that dragged her down into strange new realms of sensation.

She could feel her fingers wrenching at his hair as if to scalp him, and then they suddenly weakened and slid to the nape of his warm neck, her lips opening on an uncontrollable little moan as his mouth no longer bruised but drew her lips to his with a sensuous deliberation.

Darcy had never been kissed like this in her life ... she hadn't dreamed that anything could be so heavenly, so that nothing was real but the touch and feel of the man who held her ... and then roughly tore free of her. She gave a stifled little cry and flung an arm across her eyes. She couldn't bear to look at him ... she had hated him enough to tear out his eyes, and yet she had loved being kissed by him. It was beyond reason, like a pair of animals in the bush!

'Look at me!' he ordered.

Darcy allowed her shielding arm to fall slack at her side. She gazed up at him, into the raw gold brilliance of his eyes. His black hair was tousled on his forehead, some of it clinging there in a faint film of sweat. He thrust a hand across it impatiently.

'If that ever happens again, I'll kill you,' he said deliberately.

'Y-you did it—how could I fight you?' Her voice was husky, half lost like her dignity and self-respect. She felt the disarray of her dress and her hair, but hadn't the will-power to do anything about them.

'You provoked me,' he said, and there was a thick note in his voice that deepened its Spanish intonations almost into his chest. 'But from now on, young woman, you will be the soul of discretion. You are going to marry my brother, and no Spaniard with any sense of honour ever lays a finger on his brother's wife.'

'You're going to make me marry Ramon—after the way we've behaved?' Colour burned her cheeks even as cold fingers clutched her heart. Wife to Ramon, with some primitive part of her yearning after this hard and arrogant man. This man who would probably marry Dorina, or some other Spanish girl who could pleasure his body even if she left his heart untouched. Darcy's fingers curled her hands into balls of torment ... she still wanted to touch and feel him, and it was ... oh God, it was humiliating!

'There's lust in all of us,' he said curtly. 'I won't—can't hurt Ramon by robbing him of you. What are you?' His eyes swept her up and down. 'You are just a woman and you mean nothing to me, beyond a slim body, a swathe of pale hair, and a temper I enjoy controlling as I control that of the palomino in my stable. It's a horse you must ride one of these days. You'll look an attractive pair.'

'Go to hell,' she said tiredly, dispiritedly. She felt she couldn't fight him any more ... at least not tonight. 'You and your horses and your wine valley! You think they make you a sort of—king.'

'I'm king of this castle.' He was firmly in command of himself again, lounging there against a bedpost, a hand completely steady as it straightened his tie against his speckless shirtfront. 'As an English woman you probably don't realise the amount of authority which a Spanish *dueño* has command of. It's feudal, but a man tries not to abuse it.'

'Except in my case,' she rejoined, forcing herself to sit up and straighten her dress, so neither of them would be reminded of those wild, ungovernable moments in each other's arms. 'You're cracking your whip where I'm concerned, aren't you, *señor*? The *hidalgo* has issued his orders and I obey them or get yanked to the altar while everyone turns a blind eye to your iron hand on my wrist—even the priest, I imagine.'

'You are inclined to let your imagination run away with you, my dear.' The old gleam of mockery was back in his tawny eyes. 'You will walk up that aisle looking sweet and willing in your white gown, and Ramon will be given a new lease on the life you helped to ruin. Do I make myself understood?'

'Yes,' she said quietly. 'No one could be more explicit. I am to go to the altar with the dignity of Anne Boleyn going to the block. I am to accept the axe on my neck without a murmur. I am to live in your house as your sister-in-law, and I hope it twists your innards into knots!'

As she finished speaking a turmoil of emotion shook Darcy from head to toe, a mixture of frightened anger and that other more primitive reaction she didn't dare to think about.

Julio Valdez moved away from her with that silent, wild animal walk of his and she knew that his determination to bend her was as unbending as his own backbone. 'I daresay I shall survive such an onslaught to my system,' he drawled. 'You don't imagine, do you, that I shall be hiding a passion-torn soul each time I see you with my brother?'

'I wasn't thinking of your soul,' she flung at him. 'I don't imagine that ever gets involved where you and women are concerned.'

'What does get involved, my dear?' He swung round to face her, standing tall and dark against the rose-wood panelling of the double doors. 'I'm panting to know, so do enlighten me.'

'You know well enough.' She flung out a hand, indicating his lean hard body in the dark suiting that fitted him like a glove. 'Women are no more than a—a taste of honey to you ... but I must say it surprised me that you should have a conscience about allowing me to sleep in that other poor woman's bedroom.'

'So you think I was involved with her?' One of his black brows raised itself sardonically.

'I'm sure you were,' Darcy rejoined. 'Why else would you order me out of the room?—I think your conscience troubled you on Ramon's account. If I marry him I become a Valdez and you take that name very seriously, don't you, *señor*? You take enormous Spanish pride in its links with the old days when the conquistadors plundered Peru and made themselves rich on whatever they could steal. I daresay this house was built from plunder.'

'It assuredly was,' he agreed. 'Like many of those fine mansions in England. It's a fundamental fact of nature that the strong override the weak, but no matter how the Valdez estate came into being it has for a very long time provided employment and roots for a number of people. If I take pride in it, then I have reason to do so, and any woman taking the Valdez name as her own will adopt that same pride.'

'While the underlying scars and scandals are kept well hidden?' she murmured.

His eyes, then, were more dangerous than she had yet seen them, gleaming as if he might spring at her and prove just how ruthless he could be with a woman. A pulse fluttered hard in her throat as the menace leapt from his eyes into her very bones.

'I warned you once before not to get into a *corrida* with me,' he said. 'What are you after, eh? Are you hoping to make me so furious that I'll throw you out of San Solito?'

'You know well enough that I'm not going to fit in. Only Ramon wants me here and if he knew the truth, that I didn't come here with the intention of marrying him—he must be told the truth! I shall tell him——'

'You will keep your mouth shut,' Julio ordered. 'I was with Ramon the day the doctor had to tell him that his spine was irreparably damaged. I was there when he tried to shoot himself. He won't suffer that kind of despair again, not if I can prevent it. If you are what he needs, then he'll have you. Clad in white, carrying flowers, and looking heavenly, Miss Beaudine, even if you feel like hell.'

In the stormy silence that followed his words her face was distorted, as if she had been struck by the hand he flung out in savage emphasis. He meant every word and he looked every inch capable of making her obey them. San Solito was in the wilds and she was surrounded by people who in the Spanish tradition owed allegiance to the *dueño*. His word was law here in this remote place and there was no one she could turn to who would understand her predicament, sympathise with it, and least of all assist her in escaping from it.

Right now she was trapped in the heart of the web ... right this moment there was nothing she could do but fold her wings and try to get some sleep.

'I—I'm very tired,' she said. 'I'd be grateful if you'd go.'

'I'm going, *señorita*. I leave you to sleep on what I've said. I share blood and bone with Ramon, but you— you mean nothing to me. You mean everything to him! Understood?'

She nodded, feeling herself tremble with emotional exhaustion. She pushed tiredly at her hair which felt heavy, and here and there her body throbbed where he had bruised her. She didn't want to mean anything to him, but when he said it, it was as if he lashed at her with a whip.

He stared at her from beneath drawn brows, then with a shrug he took a cigarrillo case from his pocket and proceeded to light one. His hand reached for the door handle. 'We've talked enough for tonight. I think we understand one another, don't you? I shall tell Ramon that you're feeling tired and must get some sleep. *Hasta mañana.*'

'Goodnight.' Darcy watched the doors close behind him, leaving a blankness where his vital presence had been. Darcy felt enervated, as a person does when nervously exhausted. The feeling was so overwhelming that she could have wept. Tomorrow ... God, hurry tomorrow, for then she must get away from this place. There had to be a way, and as she pushed wearily at her hair she caught sight of herself in the mirror and remembered what Julio Valdez had said about his stables.

He had horses, plenty of them, and she had learned to ride years ago at Braintree when her father was still alive. He used to drive her to the local riding stable in his old jalopy and twice a week for an hour she would ride the lanes with other girls until she had become proficient in the saddle. Like riding a bicycle it was something a person never forgot, and though she didn't doubt that the Valdez horses were more highly-strung and tougher to handle, she was determined to have a try.

There was a tremor in her hand as she slid the zip of her dress and stepped out of it, her stockinged feet in the deep carpet, quiet as smoke to walk upon. Never in her life had Darcy slept in a room like this one, and though it was true that as Ramon's wife she would know every comfort—every material comfort—all she was concerned with was getting away from a house dominated by Julio Valdez.

Julio, always there, at the head of the table, watching her with his brother and knowing as she did that an unholy reaction to each other was there in every glance, every chance meeting in the garden courts and byways of this rambling house.

What would that do to Ramon, if there ever came a time when that devilish attraction became too strong to resist?

Darcy stood in her slip, her hair a pale tumbling mass on her shoulders, her stricken gaze on her reflection in the mirror. She was standing so when in the mirror she saw her bedroom doors open again. Her heart throbbed. 'Don't you ever knock?' she cried out.

'Have you anything to hide that I wouldn't know about?' He strolled past her carrying a steaming glass in a fretwork holder, which he placed on the table at the bedside. 'Ramon insisted that you have hot chocolate with cinnamon and a dash of cream. He wishes you a good night's sleep and requests that you take breakfast with him on the patio in the morning.'

Darcy stood there feeling almost naked as Julio flicked his eyes over her hair and figure, one strap of her slip aslant on the soft white slope of her shoulder. She felt his eyes brush across her breast and her heart was beating so madly that it made her feel dizzy.

'You really are charming,' he said softly. 'I can understand Ramon having such a crush on you. The pale blonde hair is real, eh?'

'Would you like proof, *señor*?' The words were out

of her mouth before Darcy could stop them, and instantly a flame of embarrassment seared her throat and cheeks.

'Yes, that was very naughty,' he drawled. 'There's a little streak of the hoyden in the demure Miss Beaudine, eh?'

'Please go.' She turned away from him, unable to endure his eyes that seemed to follow every line and curve of her body beneath the fragile slip of silk. She was racked with the fear that he would touch her, afraid of those sensual forces that could cloud the mind and take control of the body so that nothing mattered beyond the urge for physical pleasure. Darcy was still innocent, but the very centres of her being were aware of what it would be like to be taken and entirely possessed by this man who had flayed her with cruel words, yet who made her palpitate in every limb.

One half of her wanted him, here and now ... the other half said again, chokingly, 'Please leave my room —you offend me!'

He went, closing the doors with a sharp click. Darcy trembled. Her lips were dry and she felt as if she might faint. It was unbelievable that another human being could affect one in such a devastating way. That time in England she had been glad to get away from him and had told herself that she hoped she'd never see him again. Had she been fooling herself? Had she really known that inevitably they would meet again?

The dryness of her mouth induced her to pick up the glass of chocolate and taste it. She found it curiously pleasant and she sank down on the side of her bed and allowed herself to be soothed by the drink. Afterwards, feeling a lot less tense, she slipped into a nightdress and climbed into the large bed, with its ornately carved headrest rather like a huge Spanish fan spread out above her.

Everywhere she looked were those details which reminded her of how far away she was from the less beautiful but more reassuring objects in her London bedsitter.

Furniture with the patina of soft gold, the muted gleam of long silken window drapes, the shimmer of shaded lamps in ivory and jade-green. Darcy's gaze travelled slowly around the room, while she lay against plump pillows in soft linen covers edged with lace. She could feel the response of her body to the luxury of it all; it was her mind that rejected being here, for her mind was too vividly aware of the reason.

She couldn't ... wouldn't be swayed by pity into becoming a wife in name only!

Tonight in this very room she had discovered what her body could feel when in contact with the ruthless masculinity of Julio Valdez. Her skin, her limbs, her entire femininity had wanted to be crushed to every male inch of him. She had wanted to respond to the carnality with a wild abandon that in retrospect brought the shamed blood rushing to her cheeks.

For the first time in her life she had come up against that kind of reaction to a man and she despised the excitement it had aroused in her as much as she disliked the man who caused it. Something so savagely sensual bore no relation to love. Love was surely a splendour of the heart, a passionate surge of tenderness and desire, a ravishment of the senses that took account of liking, respect, tolerance for the person desired. Julio had aroused her to an animal sensuality ... and it could happen again if she married his brother and lived beneath his roof.

With a groan almost of pain Darcy rolled over on her face and clenched the pillow with her fingers. She had come to San Solito at his bidding, almost as if some residue of animal attraction had lingered in her unaware, implanted during that first cruel meeting with him at the hospital where Ramon had lain injured.

Julio had cracked his whip across the pages of his letter and disobeying the instinct to fly to her mother, Darcy had come to Spain ... but when morning came she had to get away again.

She moved her hot forehead in her hair and thought again of what he had said about the palomino in his stables. Yes, that's what she would do! She'd take one of his horses and ride away early from the *rancho*. There would be people working in the fields and she'd ask the way to the station ... she'd get away from him somehow. From what he did to her as a woman, and from his determination that she marry Ramon.

How could she marry Ramón when every inch of her skin still tingled from its contact with Julio!

She reached an arm to the bedside lamp and switched it off. She welcomed the darkness, for she wanted to sleep ... to sleep and forget everything for a blessed while.

A wave of tiredness swept over her and in a while she drifted off into the velvety limbo where the anxieties found relief in dreams that made very little sense ... awakening suddenly in the dead of night, with the certainty that something was wrong.

Darcy sat up, straining her eyes and ears through the darkness in order to see or make sense of what had awakened her from such a deep sleep. Her heart was thudding and her thoughts fled downstairs to Ramon.

Instinctively she knew that something was wrong with him, and throwing aside the covers she got quickly out of bed, pushed her feet into slippers and her arms into the sleeves of her robe. She hurried to the doors, opened them and stepped outside, where the gallery was softly lit by the walls lamps that were obviously not extinguished during the night. She made her way to the staircase and hurried down to the hall and was making her way across its dimness to Ramon's apartment when someone came out, looking incredibly dark in a black robe over black pyjama trousers, the sash carelessly tied so his bare upper half could be seen, the dark hair rampant on his chest.

'Darcy!' He spoke her name imperatively. 'You are wanted by Ramon—I was about to fetch you to him!'

'What's wrong?' In her anxiety she caught at Julio's arm and felt at once the hard muscles tensing under her grip.

'He has these turns—it's a kind of breathlessness brought on by tension and nerves. It almost resembles a heart attack except that it isn't one. Come, he's asking to see you! He's been in something of a state ever since you left the *sala* in such a hurry.'

Darcy gazed up at Julio, seeing his brooding eyes shadowed by his dark lashes, and the thrust of the bones against his tanned skin. For brief moments the atmosphere between them was alive with vibrations, swift missiles of thought and feeling that flew from his eyes into hers, exploding in little shafts throughout her body. She backed away from him and hurried into Ramon's bedroom.

Doña Ansonia was there ministering to him, a frail, thin figure with pillows banked behind his shoulders, and a drawn look to his face. His eyes lit up when Darcy entered and he held out a hand to her.

'Don't over-excite him,' his aunt said sharply. 'The poor boy is just beginning to relax.'

'I wanted to see you, Darcy.' Ramon caught at her hand and clung to it with febrile fingers. 'I thought you were unhappy—you seemed to be crying when you ran out of the *sala* tonight.'

'It—it was the song. My father always loved it and it brought back memories.' Darcy managed to smile at him. 'You're all right, Ramon?'

'Now you are here with me.' He drew her hand to his lips, and Darcy was aware of his aunt's look of disapproval, and of Julio standing tall near the doorway, watching the scene, knowing as she did that the strands of the Valdez web were tightening around her, binding her in bonds of pity to the young man who was in a state of nervous tension over her abrupt departure from the *sala*.

Oh God! Darcy felt the backs of her knees go weak. What would Ramon be like if she ran away from the *rancho*?

'Sit down on the bed beside me,' he urged. 'I want you nearer to me.'

'Mind,' his aunt said, 'don't disturb him too much.'

'*Amiga*,' he smiled, 'how you worry over a poor bag of bones like me!'

'It's because I love you.' She fussed with his pillows and stroked a strand of damp black hair from his brow. 'I told you the girl was being emotional, but you, my silly *niño*, had to go and get yourself into a state of anxiety over her. Where did you imagine she was going?'

'I don't know, *amiga*.' He studied Darcy, a frown wrinkling his eyebrows. 'You weren't running out on me, were you, *querida*?' he asked.

Darcy felt as if her heart turned over, for his eyes were so densely anxious, and his fingers were gripping hers with a strength which surprised her. She could hear and feel the silence and knew she had to break it, with words that would reassure him.

'Everything overwhelmed me, Ramon, that's all. I'd had a long journey, and I felt concerned for you all the way coming here. We had been such good friends in England——'

'Friends?' He grasped her hand until she almost gasped aloud as her fingers were crushed together. 'We're betrothed, Darcy. You came to me in answer to my proposal—didn't you?'

She swam for a moment in a haze of pain and wild longing to wrench free of the physical and mental strangulation. Now was the moment when she could have denied that there had ever been a proposal of marriage, but Ramon was too vulnerable, too liable to be hurt so that it brought on distressing attacks like the one he had already suffered. Even as Darcy tried to form the words that would release her from San Solito, compassion took over and she inclined her head ... and almost felt the silken knot tighten against her throat.

Ramon smiled, showing his white teeth, always so admired by the other girls at the college, who had said that with his hair, eyes and teeth, not to mention his romantic nature, he should be in films.

Instead he had ended up in a wheelchair, and with sudden reckless decision Darcy leaned forward and kissed him. His lips moved beneath hers, but it was a kiss that lacked every sensation she had felt when Julio had so thoroughly kissed her. There had been fire and fury in his kiss ... heaven and hell combined in a mindless fusion.

She felt only a gentle yet ironbound pity for his

brother ... and it was his brother she was going to marry.

'Darling Darcy,' Ramon murmured. 'I always knew you'd be mine—one day.'

Yes, she thought dimly. It had somehow been inevitable, and the witnesses to her surrender were Julio and his aunt. They watched and listened while Ramon said exultantly:

'We'll be married as soon as Julio can arrange it!' He glanced across the bedroom towards the shadows where the tall figure stood, all in black. 'You won't be tardy, will you, *amigo*? I feel that the sooner the knot can be tied, the better it will be for me. Then I can have Darcy with me night and day.'

'The arrangements will be made,' Julio promised. His voice was deep, steady as a rock, and the sound of it somehow intensified Darcy's choked feeling. The noose was around her neck and the knot was pressing into her flesh ... how she managed to smile at Ramon she never knew. But she had to smile and hide from Julio the despair she suddenly felt at being night and day with any man but him!

It was a shocking realisation and one which she had to thrust away from her by drawing Ramon closer to her, her arm enclosing his shoulders while he kissed the fingers he had crushed. Darcy gazed at his dark head bent over her hand and wondered if he had deliberately hurt her. It was an unsettling thought until he raised his eyes to hers and she saw in them the deep burning need of a man who wanted to believe that his life could still hold a woman who would belong to him alone.

Darcy knew inevitably that she would belong to Ramon ... that it had somehow been destined from that first time in music class when he had sat down

beside her and smiled as if never in his good-looking,
indulged life had he known what it felt like to be rejected by a female.

It wasn't in Darcy to reject him now ... it was Julio
Valdez whom she must learn to cast out of her thoughts
.. her longings.

CHAPTER SIX

DARCY had been taking breakfast with Ramon for over a week now. He enjoyed that leisurely hour on the patio, where the rattan table was set beneath an ancient pair of avocado trees, the leaves dappling the lace cloth and the sunlight glinting on the silver coffee pot.

The mornings were lovely at San Solito, softly cool before the heat of the southern day set in, and it wasn't in Darcy's nature to be unresponsive to the delight of walking through the colonnade that led to the walled patio where birds flitted and clouds of starry-speckled vine overhung the stonework. There were fig trees with twisted shapes, loquats and passifloras of deep purple. Huge pink tulips held sparkling beads of dew, and sprays of golden vine trailed over the shell basins of a fountain.

The tiling of the patio was laid in oriental patterns and when the sun struck across the tiles it drew from them a strange mixture of colours. Each morning the patio was watered and always a scent of water and flowers hung in the air. Yellow tangerine trees added their tangy aroma, and in the tango, a deep-golden vine, the flash of a humming-bird could sometimes be seen, for this was where they liked to hide.

Darcy crossed the Moorish tiles and felt the oriental secretiveness that overhung the patio at this time of the day ... and towards evening, when she sometimes came to sit in the loggia of Moorish design that was built into a kind of alcove, its walls of intricate lacings of iron set in plaster, its roof a small dome rising against the trees. Entrance into the loggia was by means of a key-shaped opening adorned with ironwork, and inside were white plaster walls, a deep blue curving ceiling and a bronze bell of a lamp. A white iron seat and table were placed there, and the little place offered a seclusion Darcy had need of, for it was still very disturbing the way plans were going rapidly ahead for her marriage to Ramon. The sewing woman who lived on the estate had brought materials to show her, but it was Doña Ansonia who had decided that her dress be made from a length of pure ivory satin, the design to be simple in contrast to the antique lace of the family veil she was to wear.

The veil had been reverently shown to her by Ramon's aunt, old but still exquisite, and long enough to reach to her ankles. It was in patterns of lilies, vines and swords, symbolic of the Valdez traditions, Darcy had been told. Of pure brides, of the valley vines, and the men who had fought to keep their heritage through the long years.

There was an underlying romance to it all and Darcy might have been intrigued, if she hadn't been the bride at the centre of the preparations. *El señor cura*, the local priest, had been to see her and to discuss the fact that she wasn't a Catholic but would be marrying into that faith. He had asked her very seriously if she realised the implications ... he had pointed out with all due respect that her husband-to-be was crippled and regardless of this fact she must abide by the vows she made to him, and those vows, he said quietly, would be for life because the Valdez family were strongly bound to their religion.

Darcy assured him that she had faced up to all that ... it was deep in her heart where the doubts and agonies were in conflict. It was alone in the little Moorish loggia where she battled with them, for she was committed to Ramon and there was no turning back the clock. The only thing she had stood out against was a personal acceptance of the Catholic faith. She wanted to remain a Protestant like her father, and though Doña Ansonia had protested and said that for many years the Valdez brides had been of the same faith as their husbands, it had been Julio who had surprisingly taken Darcy's side.

'We must all accept our own gods, angels and devils,' he had said. 'Leave the girl alone to be of her father's church. Where is the harm?'

'I am against it,' his aunt replied. 'Good Catholic girls know their place in a husband's home. They have respect for the laws of our faith. They don't—stray.'

Julio had raised a black eyebrow and glanced at Darcy as if amused. 'Do you intend to stray?' he had drawled.

'Not if I can help it,' she replied, and still she seemed to feel the impact of his tawny gaze, all the way down to the roots of her spine, a tingling awareness of him that lingered and wouldn't go away. It might have been easier for her if Julio hadn't been the master of this household ... yet on the other hand she sometimes wondered if it might have been harder. Reluctant though she was to admit it, he added a stimulation to the days, a stab of excitement when he entered a room, a strange awareness that despite the part he had played in bringing about her marriage to his brother, he was there to protect her from other members of his family.

He was the catalyst in her life and as such he kept her from brooding. The guilty feeling was always there

that when she smoothly combed her hair and pinned
it at one side in the style that suited her, it was because
she had seen his eyes flick her hair in the sunlight.
When, as was the case this morning, she wore her
creamy silk shirt and a tapestry print skirt in brown
and orange, it was because the garments suited her ...
and might suit his taste if he were to see her wearing
them.

A guilty sense of excitement always underlay her
outward look of composure ... it was a feeling she had
never known in her life before, half enjoyable and yet
tormenting, and something she had sworn to crush out
of herself.

She had tried, but his personality was too definite to
be ignored. The sheer impact of his physical presence
was almost akin to the savage touch of the southern
sun when it arose and lay like a golden flame in the
sky. He couldn't be shut out of her thoughts as easily
as she had hoped; he invaded them even when he was
nowhere to be seen. Suddenly a dark hawk with spread
wings would swoop across the valley and Darcy would
think of Julio. Or the sun would catch in the crest of a
towering palm and she would imagine the desert from
whence that tree had come long ago, planted here in a
Spanish garden just as the seeds of Moorish culture had
been planted in the man who in so short a time would
become her brother-in-law. That touch of the Moor
had made him ruthless, in his looks and in his outlook.
She had hurt his brother and so she must pay the
penalty. An eye for an eye, and a tooth for a tooth.

Right now the patio was quiet except for the birds,
for Ramon's male attendant hadn't yet wheeled him
from the house. Darcy welcomed these few moments of
peace before she had to perform her act as the shy
young bride-to-be.

She had always been fond of Ramon in a sisterly way and she admired his looks, but in her secret heart she despaired of what lay ahead of her. She wondered just how much courage it would take to stand at the altar and vow devotion to a man she didn't truly love. Her compensation would be this house, for she could no longer deny that it fascinated her, the Valdez stronghold whose towering gates were closed against the world each night, its traditions kept intact and not to be changed because a foreign girl came to live here. The place and the people absorbed her and the life she had lived in faraway London seemed to lose its hold on her with each passing day at San Solito.

Just as her skin was tanning in the southern sun, so was a subtle change taking place in her personality. She had begun to play Spanish music on the honey-coloured guitar and to pick up Spanish phrases. She wasn't fighting her destiny, but she was hiding what stirred in her heart when the nightingales flew up from the valley in the evenings and the star-jasmine scented the air.

She kept her eyes lowered when she played, so she wouldn't see the white cashmere of a dinner jacket covering a wide pair of shoulders. She tried to ignore the sultry murmur of Dorina's voice and the ruby glint of almond-shaped fingernails against a white-clad arm. She strove at all times to be the polite and composed English girl who wore the courtship bracelet of the Valdez *señorita*. It must never show in her manner or her eyes that when Dorina strolled in the jasmine-scented garden with the *dueño* it was as if a fine-bladed knife slid between Darcy's ribs and pierced her with pain.

Darcy despised the feelings aroused in her by Julio and to compensate for them she gave additional time and attention to Ramon. She sang and played to him whenever he was in the mood to listen. She read aloud the books he enjoyed until her throat was parched. She wheeled him around the courtyards until her arms felt loose in their sockets.

Her skin was tanning but her bones were growing more distinct as her contours grew slenderer. Darcy knew she was thinner because her cream silk shirt touched her body. She felt as if a conflict of emotions were eating her alive.

'*Buenos días.*'

She swung round, startled out of her thoughts, and there against the trunk of a palm lounged a tall figure in a dark silky shirt and fawn trousers, tailored closely to lean hips and long legs. Above the dark silk she saw the ruthless melding of power and passion in his face, and then in that silent way of his he began to cross the mosaic tiles like something out of a Moorish palace, a hand brushing at the morning glory that mantled some stonework, a lizard stirring and scurrying at his touch. Despite the power of his build he had a natural sort of grace that made him fascinating to watch when he moved.

His eyes held hers, his brief smile was tinged with something indefinable as he came to stand over her. His gaze slid down her hair, held casually at one side by a tortoiseshell clip. Darcy felt the ticking of her heart, beating away the unbearable excitement of those seconds ... when he looked at a woman he touched her ... when he said nothing, he spoke volumes with his lazy tawny eyes.

'May I say that you are a picture of *eterna primavera*.' He took her hand by the fingertips and pressed them; no Latin kissed the hand of an unmarried woman.

'*Por Dios!*' He frowned at the dark bruising across the backs of her fingers. 'How did you get these?'

'Oh—I must have knocked my hand. I—I bruise easily.' It was a lie about the way she had got the bruising. She couldn't bring herself to tell Julio that Ramon had caused it when he gripped her hand, so rigidly at times that she felt like crying out.

A fleeting concern came and went in his eyes. 'You should be more careful, *señorita*. A Spanish house is made of stone, iron and strong wood, and that's why a woman always looks graceful in Spanish surroundings. Have you now grown a little more used to San Solito?'

'Yes, thank you,' she replied politely. 'I've never known a house like this one, there's so much to discover and delight in. You must be very proud of being its master.'

'Pride and iron blend in the Spaniard as in his home.' He abruptly leaned a little closer to her and his nostrils tensed. 'You wear an intriguing perfume, fragrant yet sensual. Is it carnation?'

'Yes.' Darcy felt the warmth under her skin. 'Ramon gave it to me in a cut-glass bottle. I—I wear it to please him.'

'You do many things to please him, eh?' Julio's eyes scanned the contours of her face. 'Don't take the duties too strenuously or on the wedding day the dress won't fit you. You have lost some weight, haven't you?'

'I was never big built, *señor*.' Instinctively her eyes took in the power of his build, the silk of the dark shirt moulding the sleek muscles of his chest and shoulders. She despised herself for her female reaction to him and had to combat it with the weapon of words. 'You're bound to compare me unfavourably with the more curvaceous Latin girls in your life. Spanish men like women to be hampered by full curves and long flowing hair, don't they?'

'Hampered?' he murmured. 'That's an evocative word, *señorita*.'

'Didn't the Moors used to feed their harem favourites with stuffed dates and cream horns in order to make them so languid that all they wanted to do was laze about on silk cushions?'

'And you think that is my type of woman?' he drawled, glints of sardonic amusement in his eyes. 'A large, languid lady on a cushion, with kohl on her eyes and fingernails? Come, I think you know better than that, don't you?'

Darcy thought of him with Dorina and had to admit to herself that she did know better. This was a man who liked to ride with a woman; who liked to trigger off her emotions and bring out the temper and vivacity in her. Darcy knew full well that his Moorish ancestors hadn't implanted in him their fondness for the odalisque, the concubine who had no will of her own and was merely a heap of curves and limbs to be caressed.

'You see, you smile just faintly.' He placed a finger against the edge of Darcy's mouth, where the lip had quirked. 'You know that passive submission in a woman holds no appeal for me, though I'm sure you would like to believe that I'm entirely the male brute with none of the finer feelings.'

'I think your feelings are well armoured, *señor*.' Still he was holding his finger against her face and Darcy was more intensely aware of that slight contact than she was ever aware of having her arm or neck stroked by Ramon. She wanted to jerk away from Julio but thought it wiser not to move. He mustn't ever know that she found his touch so deeply disturbing ... play-

ing upon sensual chords within her that wanted more
... so much more.

'You think me a hard man, eh?' His eyes scanned her
face, the lashes dark against the tawny centres. 'You
believe yourself a victim of my tyranny, is that it?'

'If you already know the answer to your own ques-
tion then why ask me, *señor*?'

'So I'm cast in the role of tyrant, eh?'

'A suitable one.' Her eyes swept him from head to
foot, she hoped with sufficient scorn to convince him
that she found him entirely dislikable. 'You were born
for the role, most men are who can take control of a
large estate and make it a paying proposition. Your
aunt was telling me that at the time of your father's
death the estate was going downhill.'

'That is so.' His eyes roved the sheen of her hair
against her cheek. 'As you imply, it takes a certain
strain of ruthlessness to make a success of a business
and my father lost much of his interest in San Solito
after my mother was killed.'

Darcy caught her breath, for up until now she had
assumed that the former mistress of San Solito had
died naturally.

'So you didn't know?' he murmured. 'Ramon has
never discussed it?'

Darcy shook her head. 'He doesn't talk much of
family matters, *señor*.'

Julio studied her face, then raked his fingers through
his dark hair. 'Ramon has a twin sister, as you know.
They were about seven at the time and the boy decided that he'd put Raquel up on Madre's horse Santana because he went like the wind. Ramon then
mounted along with the girl and they set off. All might
have been well, but it was one of those sultry days with

some thunder in the air and Santana suddenly bolted. As it happened a fool of a stable hand had seen the children playing about with the horse but had made no attempt to stop them. When Madre came to the stable for her mount and found him gone, the fool then informed her that the children had made off on his back. My mother took another horse and rode off in search of the children, feeling sure that Santana would take the same route she and the horse always took of a morning, a path that encircled the valley and went off into the wooded hills. She took a short cut in order to try and head off Santana. A gate was closed and she made her mount leap it ... he flung her from the saddle in the direct path of the galloping Santana, whose flying hooves kicked her and killed her, there in front of the terrified twins. When the workers came up from the valley, hearing the screams of the children, they found them with Santana beside the dead woman.'

Julio paused and drew the breath deeply through his nostrils. 'My father had the poor beast of a horse shot dead, though had I not been away at school I think I could have talked him out of it. Madre wouldn't have wanted that to happen. Ramon was also punished by being locked up alone in one of the bedrooms for a number of hours. My father was out of his mind with grief and I believe had Ramon not been locked out of his sight—you understand me?'

Darcy nodded, for since coming to San Solito she had discovered that Latin people had a deep, almost primitive core at the centre of their emotions. That they loved and hated with equal fierceness, and their family bonds were close and strong. On this estate there were a number of people who had jobs and dwellings because they were distantly related to the main family. It was traditional in the south, almost feudal, with one man at the head of the clan whose word was accepted as law.

Long ago a boy of seven had been locked away from the *dueño* for his own safety ... Ramon who never talked of his boyhood because it was overshadowed by the guilt implanted in him by his father's grief-stricken anger. For hours as it grew darker the boy would have crouched alone with his tears ... the brother who might have protected him had been far away at school.

Her eyes dwelt consideringly on Julio's face and she found herself wondering if the protection he now gave Ramon was extra strong in order to make up for what happened all those years ago. Was he so firm, so adamant in his protection because he couldn't forget the lonely terror of a small boy whose game had turned into a grim reality?

'What happens to us as children has a strong influence on what we become as adults,' he said. 'I was sixteen when that happened, and by the time I was eighteen I was running San Solito.'

'I see.' Darcy spoke quietly and glanced away from him to where the sun was in the crown of the trees so they seemed afire. She heard the cooing of doves in the alcoves of a white *palomar* and the water tumbling in the basins of the fountain. The beauty of the house was impregnated with its joys and sorrows, and she would become part of all this because Julio had to put his brother before any woman ... even a woman he might want himself.

'As you can see, San Solito is worth its sacrifices,' he murmured.

Darcy saw a gracious building, which obviously meant more to Julio than a woman could hope to mean. He seemed to admire Dorina in the same way, as if her looks and lines held more appeal for him than her character; he was too shrewd to be blind to the fact that she was high-handed, vain, and with a rather spiteful edge to her wit.

'Your father obviously cared more for a human being,' Darcy remarked. 'I expect Ramon takes more after him than you do.'

'I expect he does.' Julio's smile was brief and enigmatical. 'Soon it will be Easter and you'll become a Valdez bride. I understand from Ansonia that the dress will be quite stunning.'

'I think Ramon will be pleased.' As Darcy spoke a tremor of coldness travelled along the very marrow of her bones and the backs of her knees turned liquid. Because there was no one in Spain to act the part, it had been decided that Julio should give her away. It was to be his hand which officially handed her to Ramon at the altar and even to imagine that moment was to anticipate the panic Darcy knew she would feel. Even yet it seemed hardly real that it was going to happen ... the most profound occasion in a girl's life when she should be radiant with expectation, filled with hope and longing, wildly desirous of being part of the man who placed his gold ring on her finger.

Oh yes, the dress was going to be stunning, but Darcy felt like a dummy when the women fussed around her and made the corrections that would ensure its perfection when the morning of the wedding came. It was all being done to please Ramon ... Darcy knew that her desires weren't given a second's thought.

Her desires that so alarmed her whenever she found herself alone with the man who was going to give her away. She yearned to crush them out of existence, but they were too alive, leaping the defences she put up against them. Right now her gaze couldn't seem to pull

away from his tanned chest in the deep opening of his
shirt ... the very tips of her fingers vibrated with the
urge to touch him and find him warm and vibrant as
Ramon could never be.

That the mere look of him could so disturb her made
Darcy react with a passionate resentment. 'What if an
earthquake came and ruined all this?' she asked.

'I'd be furious,' he replied, 'and then I'd start to build
again. It's for women to weep.'

'You're too big and strong, is that it, *señor*? Too
much the *macho* Spaniard to show any kind of weakness? Oh, how marvellous to be so invulnerable! It
must make you feel superior to everyone!'

'*Dios——*' The dark hair raked his forehead and his
eyes gleamed tigerishly. 'Don't try me too far—I warn
you!'

'What will you do? Treat me to a withering lecture
on how to bow and scrape to the master of San Solito?
I'm marrying Ramon, but I don't intend to become
like your aunt who worships every bit of furniture,
every scrap of lace, every silver utensil in this house as
if it has a soul. Only people have feelings—most people,
that is.'

'You think I haven't any feelings?' His nostrils were
dangerously tensed and a nerve was hammering against
his lower lip. 'Go on, have the courage to accuse me
of being a mere automaton.'

'I believe you are,' she said recklessly. 'You've
ploughed all your feelings into San Solito, distilled
them into your golden wine, bred them into your
Arabian horses—how can you know what it feels like
to stare into the darkness and dread the daylight when
you have to behave as if everything were normal when
you know that it never can be!'

Oh, she had said too much, and with a half-choked cry Darcy turned away from him, crying out when his hand caught her by the shoulder and wrenched her around to face him. She felt his fingers biting into her, to her very bones.

'I probably know more than you think.' His grip slackened and his hand slid suddenly down her back to the centre of her waist, pressing her to him so she felt the hardness of his muscles. 'Men who fly aircraft have a saying, they call it the point of no return, when if they turn back they court disaster, when if they fly on they may reach some sort of a haven. You and I are at the point of no return. We crossed that line when you came to Spain, for we both know that you had a choice. You could have gone out to South Africa to your mother and sought the protection of her husband, who I understand is an Embassy official. Instead you came to San Solito and you have to accept the consequences—fate will see to it, as we say.'

'It was your letter that left me little choice.' Darcy could feel him against her and even as she wanted to break the contact she couldn't bear to pull away from the potent warmth of him ... so alive, so quick with danger and a forbidden delight.

'W-what did you do with the letter—burn it?' Her voice trembled though she was fighting to keep her body rigid.

'Yes,' he said shamelessly. 'As you guessed I took it from your bag and later on I tore it into pieces and put them on the kitchen fire. I don't believe you would have shown the letter to Ramon, but I couldn't risk it.'

'You're a very ruthless man, Julio Valdez.' Darcy could feel a treacherous weakness in her body, a need of the senses to experience that ruthlessness in a physical way. She felt ashamed of herself and wanted to hate him ... hate him for making her feel this way.

'I don't think you'd stop at much in order to get what you feel is due to a Valdez,' she said, an edge to her voice. 'The rich are always heartless and the poor have to take it, or go hungry.'

'*Por Dios*, but you go far!' His hand pressed against her spine and Darcy felt in him sufficient strength to break her in half. The feeling alarmed and excited her, and it was the excitement that drove her even further, using words to try and combat what he did to her in a physical way.

'It's true, isn't it, *señor*? You are one of the privileged demi-gods who has only to snap his fingers in order to have flunkies and women leaping to obey the slightest order. You think you've fitted me into that category and made me afraid of your frown and your big broad shoulders!'

'You're afraid, *niña*.' His voice was low in his throat and for endless moments his gaze held hers, penetrating her to the depths of her body. 'Not of my frown but of my favour.'

'Your conceit is only matched by your arrogance,' she rejoined. 'You're the very last man——'

'Don't continue with that cliché unless you mean it,' he drawled. 'A man and a woman who can spark each other to temper are two people who can set off more explosive reactions in each other. You know it as well as I do, and it's just as well we do know it.'

'I only know one thing for certain.' Darcy flung the hair out of her eyes. 'I've hated your attitude ever since that time in England when I begged to see Ramon after the accident and you said it would be like giving him a dose of poison to take me to his bedside. Do you

eally imagine you can say that to someone and expect
her to *like you*?'

'I've never expected you to like me.' He actually
smiled, as if enjoying a secret joke. 'It would surprise
me if you did.'

'And yet you imply that we——' She dragged her
gaze from his and fixed it upon the lacy outlines of the
locust trees. She was intensely aware of his hand pressing hard against her backbone and of the sensation
that pressure induced, forcing her so near to him that
she could feel the power and potency in his body. She
wondered if in doing this he was cruelly reminding
her that her husband-to-be could never strain her to
his body and make her aware of the dangerous joys to
be got from a man.

The sudden awfulness of the comparison gave her the
strength to drag herself away from Julio. Where he had
touched her was a flayed feeling, as if she left part of
herself there in his hand, but just in time had she
wrenched away from him. Someone called her name
and she saw Ramon being wheeled from beneath the
colonnade by his attendant. She awaited their approach
with a pounding heart, distrusting her legs which felt
as if the strength had been drained from them. Julio
casually smoothed his hair and looked, as always, in
total control of himself.

He strolled towards his brother and took hold of the
wheelchair. 'I'll see to this,' he said. 'You go along and
have your own breakfast, Gomez.'

'*Si, señor.*' The attendant scrutinised Ramon to make
sure he was all right, then he walked back towards the
house, leaving Darcy alone with the brothers.

Ramon swept his eyes up and down her slim figure.
'How attractive you are looking, *chica*.' He smiled up

at her. 'Aren't you going to give me a kiss? You aren't
shy of Julio, are you?'

'Certainly not,' she said, and bending over Ramon
she lightly touched her lips to his cheekbone.

'Ah, can't you do better than that?' he mocked
softly. 'Your lips would feel sweet on mine, and give
me an appetite for breakfast.'

Darcy couldn't refuse him the more intimate kiss,
but all the time she was conscious of Julio watching her
with his brother, assessing the warmth of her kiss, or
the lack of it. Rebellion flared inside her and added
fuel to a fire she didn't really feel.

'Ah,' a low groan came from Ramon. 'How I wish
—ah, *Dios*, how I long to be a man again!'

'You are a man.' Darcy spoke fervently. 'A very brave
one!'

'No.' He shook his dark head and his eyes were glittering with anguish. 'It isn't brave of me to tie a young
and active woman to my log of a body. It would be
brave if I could cut you loose—I tell you my heart
burns!'

'Ramon, please——' She pressed his shoulder and
felt the quivering in him. 'There's no need for you to
say these things, or to even think them.'

'How can I help but think? I can't really feel any
more, and my head is filled with all sorts of questions
with tormenting answers. You are young and lovely—
made for a real man. Made for someone like Julio!'

The shock of the words went all the way through
Darcy, a barb that struck at her deepest sensibilities and
lodged there. 'No,' she said fiercely, her eyes fixed on
Ramon because she didn't dare to look at Julio. 'You
mustn't speak like that. It isn't right——'

'In every way it looks right.' He spoke almost with
irony. 'Your fair head comes just to his shoulder, do

ou know that? He's strong and whole and able to give
girl everything that I can't. Do you imagine I haven't
ooked at the pair of you and imagined you in each
ther's arms?'

'Ramon!' It was both a plea and a protest. 'I shall go
ndoors if you're going to carry on like this. You're
mbarrassing your brother.'

'Embarrass Julio?' Ramon glanced at his brother, a
wisted little smile on his mouth. 'Is that what I'm
oing, brother?'

'You're behaving like a bit of a brat,' Julio began to
vheel the chair towards the breakfast table, there in the
hade of the avocado trees. 'I wouldn't care to think
f you being cruel to your *novia*.'

'Why not, Julio?' Ramon twisted around so he could
ook at the other man. 'She's charming, isn't she?
'ou've noticed the sheen on her hair and the silky
oftness of her skin. You'd like her for yourself,
vouldn't you, big brother?'

'Don't be a young fool.' Julio spoke sternly. 'What
ou need is a good breakfast inside you.'

'What I need is to be able to use these.' Ramon
humped his legs. 'Put yourself in my seat, Julio.
Vouldn't you compare yourself to an active man if you
ad to sit about like this? Wouldn't you become frus-
rated and suspicious——?'

'I can assure you, Ramon, that your *novia* is de-
oted to you.' Julio closed a firm hand upon his
rother's shoulder. 'You know her better than I do. Did
ne flirt with other men in England?'

Ramon's gaze dwelt rather broodingly upon Darcy
nd she couldn't help noticing how Julio's dark vitality
nade him seem all the more fragile. The comparison
roused her pity, but it couldn't reach those troubled
eeps in herself where more primitive feelings had

been awakened by Julio. She felt torn in two, the com
passionate half of herself fighting to control the sensua
longings she had no right to feel.

'People change,' Ramon murmured, 'especially her
in Spain. The sun is cooler in England. There is no
scent of tangerine and jasmine, no siesta behind
lowered blinds while the sun touches everything with
its savage lust. How can any man tell what goes on in
the lovely head of a woman? How can anyone tell i
she's as angelic as she looks?'

'Snap out of this, Ramon.' A commanding note had
come into Julio's voice. 'You have the girl you wanted
and she's going to become your wife. Beyond that
amigo, what can any man do?'

'Meaning I shall never walk, eh? It's all right, Julio
I know you'd give me an arm or a leg if I asked fo
them—just see to it that you give me my wife and don'
long for any part of her for yourself.'

'Ramon, for heaven's sake!' Darcy gasped, shocked
to the core to hear the words spoken aloud ... tha
Julio might desire a part of her for himself.

'Don't be modest,' Ramon mocked her. 'Right now
you look good enough to eat, so just imagine how
delicious you are going to look in virginal white or
your wedding day. There is one thing for sure, once
you are my wife you can never be my brother's.'

Darcy stared at him, unnerved by his mood, and
mystified by his words.

'If I ever die,' Ramon said, almost brutally, 'Julio
can't have you in my place. It isn't allowed. A man
can't marry his brother's widow in Spain.'

'Ramon, you've gone far enough!' Julio thundered
the words. 'I don't know what has put these crazy
notions into your head, but the sooner you get them

out again the better for all of us. You insult your young woman. My skin is thicker, but she——'

'She has soft white skin, eh?'

'Here comes breakfast!' Darcy said it fervently as a manservant came out from the shade of the colonnade carrying a laden tray, followed by a young maid with napkin-wrapped rolls in a basket and a dish of fruit. The coffee and the food were set out on the table and when Darcy sat down she could feel herself trembling with reaction. She half expected Julio to stride off and leave her alone with Ramon and was strangely gratified when he took a chair himself and sat down, requesting of the maid that she bring another cup and saucer.

'I might as well join you both as everything looks so good,' he said. 'I usually make do with a roll and a dash of jam, and then have a snack around mid-morning. Ah, this looks enjoyable.'

It was a creamy kind of scrambled egg, with truffle chopped into it and pieces of tomato.

'Very nourishing,' Ramon said wryly. 'They make me eat it every morning in the hope that I'll put on some weight.'

'Then tuck in,' Julio urged. 'Come, Darcy, you must eat as well.'

In a ray of sunlight their glances met briefly, then broke apart. There was something in his eyes that seemed to touch her deep down, where her feelings were so vulnerable and so desperate to remain undetected. She had to make herself eat the food. She had to behave as naturally as possible.

'This is good, isn't it, Ramon?' She reached out and touched his hand, and dark against her fine-boned fingers were those bruises Julio had observed. She carefully withdrew her hand and smiled at Ramon, silently

pleading with him to trust her ... trying not to feel
the guilty weight on her heart. She would never hurt
him ... it was Julio she must hurt if she was to keep
at bay those bitter-sweet longings her marriage in name
only could never satisfy.

CHAPTER SEVEN

THE moon was huge and awesomely beautiful and the cicadas in the palm trees had set up a chorus to it. A blue lotus swirled on the surface of the pool deep in the heart of the garden, like a lonely dancer in softly gleaming skirts. And there was no season for the Andalusian roses that bloomed constantly, looking as if fashioned of velvet in the moonlight, mingling their scent with that of the dark green camphor trees. A large white moth settled on the petals of a rose and a firefly dropped like a star among the pale masses of jasmine.

Dense black shadows and silvery shafts of moonlight . . . a night made for romance.

Darcy paused at the edge of the pool and watched the silent dance of the lotus flower. There was in the air the almost magical hush that a full moon brings with it, and nearby a huge old Judas tree overhung the water, its boughs laden with red flowers. All at once Darcy had felt compelled to slip away from the family celebration that was taking place the evening before her marriage. She had set down the wine which seemed to leave a bitter taste in her mouth and had quietly retreated from the *sala* while Dorina was dancing a tango with Julio.

Still their Spanish image lingered in Darcy's mind, Dorina in a dress that clung until it reached her legs where the rose silk flared into frills; Julio in black jacket and pants, his shirt front as white as his teeth as he swung the *boleadoras* so that the leather thongs and weights caught his partner expertly around the slim waist and held her to him while they danced. With faultless Latin grace they executed the steps of the tango, the music provided by the musicians who had come to the house that evening.

Tomorrow evening dozens of people from the estate and the village would be at San Solito to help celebrate the wedding, but tonight the party was a private one. Tonight Darcy had seen Julio drink a lot of wine until his black hair was tousled on his forehead and he hadn't refused when Dorina demanded that he dance with her in the manner of a *vaquero*, the men who used the *boleadoras* to subdue horses and women alike.

Darcy had watched until in a sudden torment she could no longer stand the sight of the sleek, rose-clad body bound to his from the hips downward. She had fled, taking with her the galling knowledge that it was jealousy which had made it impossible for her to remain and watch the dance to its conclusion, when she knew Julio would bend Dorina over his arm and kiss her lips.

Even to imagine that finale was a torment that dug its claws in Darcy. She hadn't known that she could be so jealous of another woman, yet here she stood, racked by a mental image of Dorina so openly and sensuously enjoying her close contact with Julio. A physical contact permitted by the dance and the pulsating rhythm of the music, an evocation of passionate longing, of a woman whose every movement was controlled by the man, a vibrant, almost shameless yielding of herself as if it didn't matter to her that people watched and might guess that she wanted in reality the dominance which Julio displayed in the dance.

Darcy felt not a fragment of doubt that Dorina wanted Julio ... enraptured by the dance, she had shown in her darkly glowing eyes that she felt confident of having him. In every kind of way they were well matched, and both from this southern region which endowed them with similar loyalties and ideals ... a mutual pride and passion.

They had breathed and moved as if meant for each other, and Darcy had seen the approving looks bestowed upon them by members of the family. Because Ramon had sat there so intently focused upon the dancers, Darcy had been able to slip away without being observed, hastening far into the garden until she could no longer hear the beat of the music.

The moon hung molten gold above the trees, but the air felt softly cool, a fragrance which brushed her neck and arms like silk. The minutes were ticking away the hours and inexorably her freedom was slipping out of her hands even as she stood here. She took a half-frightened breath and held a hand to her heart that pounded with the desperation of something trapped. At noon tomorrow Julio would place her hand in his brother's and from that moment he would become a brother to her.

Darcy didn't want Julio for a brother ... she wanted like Dorina to be locked to his lithe body, to feel every inch of him alive and urgent with the desire to overwhelm her.

Alone here except for the gliding night moths, Darcy allowed the painful truth to come to the surface, unlocked from its prison deep inside her ... she wanted to feel the force of Julio's passion, sweeping over her so there was nothing beyond the sheer gratification of the senses. Close, close in his arms, protected for a while from the fears she must feel tomorrow, when she married a man because she pitied him.

'You fool—you fool!' she whispered to herself, not because of the pity for Ramon but because of the passion for Julio.

'*La noche está bella.*'

Darcy felt an erratic throb of the heart and of its own accord her body turned towards the voice. He stood beneath the arching bough of a tree and his long shadow slanted across the moonlit patio. The heavy roses brooded in scent and shadow, mingling their perfume with the smoke of the cigarrillo he held between his teeth.

She stood there with the pool at her heels, poised for flight as she felt the panic rising in her ... and the emotional excitement of merely seeing him, the black hair still in disarray upon his forehead, his jacket flung open as if to cool his body after the dance. From across the patio his eyes were fixed upon her face, glittering like a waiting tiger's.

'Why did you run away?' he asked. 'Wasn't the entertainment to your liking?'

'Y-you dance well, *señor*.' The quaver in her voice wouldn't be controlled. 'But it was warm in the *sala* and I needed a breath of fresh air.'

'I thought you might have disapproved of the dance.' He took the cigarrillo from his lips and the smoke seemed to lose itself in his skin. 'It originated in Argentina, among the tough horsemen who after a week in the saddle are glad to get into town for some amusement, only they become so attached to the *boleadoras* that they use them even when they dance with a woman. It might strike an English girl as symbolic of capture and submission. I couldn't help wondering when I no longer saw you standing by the red curtain in your pale dress.'

'I should hardly have thought you'd notice me, *señor*.' Her pulse was beating madly because he had noticed. 'You seemed far too enthralled.'

'It's said of a Spaniard that he can dance and work out the details of a business deal at one and the same time. We do it like breathing. You've surely danced with Ramon?'

'In a lighthearted way,' she admitted, 'but not—not as you were just dancing with Dorina.'

He raised a quizzing eyebrow and drew in a deep intake of smoke. 'You think there was something significant in the way we danced together?'

'Wasn't there?' she challenged him. 'It looked meaningful to me, *señor*.'

Suddenly his left hand moved into view and the moonlight played on the gleaming weights of the *boleadoras* and the leather lash. Suddenly Darcy felt threatened and forgetful that the pool was behind her she took a step backwards and even as she felt herself losing balance there was a whining sound and the thin leather thongs were wrapped around her waist and Julio's strong wrist was jerking her out of harm's way. With a gasp she felt both the bite of the leather and then the sudden strength of his arm around her.

'No!' she gasped. 'Please—don't!'

But silently he pushed her head against his shoulder and brought his mouth down against hers, crushing to a whimper the little cry she gave. His lips were hard, smoky, searching hers until she had no will to resist him. An almost desperate surge of longing swept through her blood and her parted lips clung to his as she submitted to the demanding intimacy of his mouth, sending ripples of sensation down through her body until her legs were so weak that she would have fallen had he released her.

He drew her closer until in her soft-skirted dress she was pressed to the length and breadth of him. It was wrong ... and yet here in the gold blaze of the moonlight it was inevitable ... a night made for love, except that she was the betrothed of Ramon and it should have been Dorina whose throat was bared for his seeking lips.

'Julio—no——' she whispered. 'Let's stop this——'

'I can't,' he breathed unevenly. 'I am dying for you!'

'How—how can you say that?' Her head felt light, as if she had been given strong wine to drink, and she felt the warm pulsating energy in him that wouldn't be reined in for very much longer, not if she allowed him this close contact of lips, warm hands, long muscular legs that had taken all the strength from hers.

'Y-you've been drinking——' She attempted to pull away from him. 'You're behaving like this with me because Dorina has to be respected——'

'Be silent,' he growled. 'What has the respectful feeling for relatives to do with us? *Dios mío*, to see you standing by those curtains looking so cool and distant when I want you to burn—burn as I do because tomorrow must come, and all the tomorrows when I can't do this to you!' He ran his hard fingers over the soft contours of her body and she saw the moon agleam in his eyes and felt the instant response of her senses.

It was the instinct to respond which gave her the strength to tear herself out of his arms, but she had forgotten the thongs of the *boleadoras*, still wrapped about her waist and making her a prisoner even as she thought she was free. Julio laughed very low in his

throat and seizing her by the arms he forced them behind her, holding her helplessly arched as he leaned
down and brushed his lips over her mouth, which she
kept tightly closed, defying him to the last ditch ...
denying herself the pleasure she longed for.

'Sweet fool, there is only the moon to see us, but we
can find ourselves some darkness if that will make
you feel more relaxed.' And even as she felt the sensual
weakness in her knees, he swept her up in his arms
and strode with her through the garden, beneath the
archway where the star-jasmine clung, towards the key-
shaped entrance to the Moorish loggia. It was dim inside and redolent of the night scents, and suddenly
there was no controlling the passion they had felt from
the moment he had asked if she had brought to Spain
a wedding dress in which to marry his brother.

It locked them relentlessly together in the darkness,
a relief and a guilty torment, a longing and a need to
touch and be touched. Ravishment and betrayal, stolen,
mad-sweet pain and pleasure.

Her fingernails stabbed and her soft moan was
stifled by his lips ... sweet, wild hurting and giving
until there was nothing ... nothing but Julio and being
part of the wild throbbing heart of him.

When the danger and excitement reached their
peak he pushed her away from him, one hand holding
her to the cool tiles of the wall. She rested there quivering, the disarrayed hair falling into her dazed eyes. She
could feel the desire burning inside her and her shoulder was bare beneath the chiffon where his touch was
more intimate than anything she had ever known.

The moon had shifted so its rays now invaded the
loggia, casting soft shadows and showing her the lashes
half-lowered over his eyes, which held a slumbrously

sensuous look. Still the emotion was barely controlled between them, still she was acutely sensitive to the barest pressure of his body against hers.

'Lovely hair, thick and soft like a puma's pelt.' He pushed his fingers through her hair and there was a thickness in his voice, a blurring of the usual conciseness. 'I want to do everything to you, do you know it?'

'W-when a man's been drinking——' Darcy took a breath, forcing out the words, 'any woman's fair game, isn't she?'

'For that I should beat the breath out of you.' His eyes didn't leave her face, searching it with a sensual intentness. 'You wanted me to do everything—do you imagine I could be fooled? I'm no teenage boy who doesn't yet know his own biology or that of the woman in his arms.'

'Oh, you're very experienced, *señor*.' She had to say these things or leave her heart entirely unprotected. Julio didn't love her ... he just felt like having her. Fair game! Her heart twisted. A woman on the eve of being wed to a man who couldn't make love to her ... normally.

Still watching her, he drew a finger down her face and fitted the tip of it into the soft cleft at the base of her chin ... Darcy stood there rigidly and fought the feeling that went through her, to the very centre of her body. The compulsion to press herself against him was intense, inviting again those sweet, wild, intimate caresses.

If she moved the fraction of an inch she knew that hell and heaven would be let loose ... she saw the threat of it smouldering in his eyes as they travelled down her neck to the movement of her breast.

'Don't look so anxious.' His laughter was softly taunting. 'I have myself in hand again—don't think I don't know myself, *amiguísima*. The *amor loco* comes out in the Valdez men now and again, inherited from those cruel Arab horsemen who came here long ago looking for young girls for their pleasure. Instinctively I brought you here, to this Moorish loggia, with its shades of the past.'

He glanced around him, letting his gaze travel upwards to the dome where the moonlight tried to enter, stabbing here and there through the lozenge-shaped glass. 'Women have been seduced here,' he murmured.

Of its own self Darcy's left hand pressed itself to her heart. The timid governess, she thought, who hadn't been able to resist the dark fascination of this Spaniard in whom were irrevocably sown the instincts of those desert horsemen who had come riding along the gorges of Spain long ago, falcons on their wrists and a tigerish glint in their eyes ... no woman would have been safe from them....

As no woman was safe from Julio Valdez!

And as if he knew what was going through her mind he suddenly swung her back into his arms until not even a shred of moonlight could have come between them and there was in his kiss the violence of not wanting to stop ... of no longer caring that in the morning she married his brother.

'Is this—is this *droit du seigneur*?' she gasped, when for a moment he freed her lips so she could catch her breath.

He was very still, and then he pushed her roughly away from him. 'You are right,' he said, 'I have been drinking too much of the valley wine. You must allow me to apologise, *niña*.'

Darcy stood there dumbly, still feeling as if his kiss was burning into her lips and making her entire body weak with longing. Half of her didn't care that she was just another woman to him ... half of her despised both of them for giving way to passions so illicit and voluptuous, part of the night, the Spanish moon, the fact that when morning came his family would dress her as his brother's bride.

'W-we were both at fault, *señor*.' Darcy fled away from him, her legs gaining strength as she neared the house. A strength she needed when as she entered the hall, intent on reaching the stairs before she was seen, someone spoke her name.

At the sound of the voice her blood seemed to freeze. All she could think of was that her hair was disarrayed and her mouth was smudged from Julio's kisses. Dorina would take one look at her and guess that she'd been with him.

'Have you seen Julio?' Dorina demanded. 'I've been looking for him—I needed to go to the bathroom and he just seemed to vanish.'

'I expect he's having a smoke.' Darcy smoothed her hair as casually as possible and kept on moving towards the staircase, keeping her face averted from Dorina's sharp eyes.

'Where have you been?'

'Oh, looking at the moonlight. I—I wanted to be alone for a little while——'

'Alone?'

'Yes——' Darcy ran the tip of her tongue around her lips, which still felt guiltily the impression of Julio's. 'The moon is huge tonight, quite awesome.'

'Did it make you feel romantic?' There was a click of high heels as Dorina began to approach Darcy, who knew that certain things were showing in her eyes that it would be fatal for the other woman to see. That interlude in the Moorish loggia had left its mark ... and there was also something very private about it that fire and rack wouldn't have dragged from her mouth.

'All that wine——' She gave a tentative laugh. 'Now it's my turn to go upstairs.'

Darcy sped away, aware that Dorina couldn't catch up with her in those heels which were so high and narrow, making her ankles look perfect beneath the hem of her dress when she had danced with Julio. Something twisted inside Darcy ... oh God, he had no right ... no right to dance that way with one woman and then come seeking her out in order to slake passions that went no deeper than his tawny skin. The things he had said to her, about dying for her, about burning for her, they had all been said to other women in order to make weak fools of them. The way he danced, the way he kissed ... just a practised seducer, she told herself stormily, who hadn't the decency to leave his brother's *novia* alone!

She entered her bedroom and switched on the lights. She was drawn to the mirror as if to a magnet, needing and hating to see what lay in her eyes after being in Julio's arms. She stood there staring at herself, at the passionate flare to her nostrils, the kiss-bruised look of her mouth, the wild light in her eyes beneath the tumbling hair. She could still feel his skin against her own, his hands on her body, the force and potency she had not been able to resist there in the scented darkness of the loggia.

It was a sensual captivation which had nothing to do with the heart, and as she lifted her hair away from her brow she remembered the deep sound of his voice as he likened her hair to the gold of a puma's pelt.

Darcy gathered her hair at the crown of her head, baring the slim neck around which he had closed a hand in a half-threat a moment before burying his lips in the smooth skin of her throat. There in the mirror she saw the look of pleading in her eyes ... how was she going to be a wife to Ramon in the same house as Julio? Each time their eyes met as if casually, the memory of tonight would be there in the room, the way they had kissed, the way they had touched, the long hard length of him pressing into her.

Engulfed in a wave of misery and guilt, Darcy flung herself on the bed, gripping the covers with hands that still felt the warm strength of masculine shoulders. With a deep sigh she turned on her back and gazed up at the ceiling ... she was going to be married to Ramon in the morning and from the moment she spoke the Latin vows in the chapel she would be bound to him as if by irons, a prisoner of his love, with her heart beating at the bars that kept her from Julio.

The memory of every merciless moment swept over her and she lay there wanting him as she hadn't known it was possible to want any man ... a shameless, racking torment that made her twist and turn as if in the grip of a fever.

Her body felt racked by an ache that started deep inside her and spread inexorably through her system, a dark despair against which she had no defence. Even at the time of Ramon's accident she hadn't felt this sort of turmoil. She had been sorry and shocked, but this was something far more primitive, as if from the very core of her a living thing was being torn out by the roots.

It wasn't to be borne, and she slid from the rumpled bed and walked restlessly to the window, where the cool night air stole in from the garden where the moon still painted the trees and flowers with splashes of silver. She leaned there wearily and though she knew that Ramon would be wondering what had become of her it was too much of an effort to move. When something alien and warm slid across her right foot she barely noticed it and took it for a fold of the curtain until it made a sibilant, hissing sound.

Darcy glanced downwards and stood transfixed by the speckled object that writhed and slid its coils on the creamy carpet. Her heart gave a thud and though she wanted to scream and run she couldn't move a muscle nor take a step as the snake opened and closed its gap of a mouth and she saw the fangs pulsating.

When it struck at her, burying its sharp fangs in the side of her ankle, she made a choked sound and fled across the room to the door, feeling the trickle of blood down her skin and the stinging pain of the bite.

Scared half out of her wits, Darcy ran along the gallery to the stairs, her heart pounding in her ears as she sped downwards to the hall, crying out the only name that mattered to her in this crisis. Julio swung round, breaking off his conversation with Carlos.

'Julio ...' This time his name was faint in her mouth. 'I—I've been bitten by a snake ...'

The lights dazzled and Darcy was aware of pitching forward a moment before he leapt and caught hold of her.

'My ankle——' A deadly nausea was gripping her stomach and a dark faintness was overtaking her, the skin of her face blanched and cold as she gazed up at Julio. She had the certain feeling that she was going to die in his arms, except that his chin was like rock and his eyes a blaze of gold as he spoke in rapid Spanish to Carlos, who raced across the hall and flung open the door of Julio's office, into which Darcy was carried and then carefully laid down on the big leather couch.

Carlos had opened a cupboard and was handing Julio a box. There were other voices that came in waves to

Darcy, people hurrying into the room and creating an atmosphere of concern. Hands touched, nylon ripped, and the darkness was clouding Darcy's mind as her leg was bared. The lamplight made painful shards of brightness against her eyelids and her body jerked as a needle plunged into her flesh. Hands held her still and her faintness became absolute as a sharp cutting pain sped up her leg into her groin.

Shaded light bathed her eyelids and the cool fragrance of cologne was in her nostrils. She stirred and was aware of the soft comfort of her bed as her eyes focused on the person who was touching her temples with the cologne.

That person was unknown to her, but the face was calm and pleasing and framed in the white starched linen of a nurse's cap.

'The patient is now awake, *señor*.' The nurse smiled and smoothed Darcy's hair. 'Her fever has almost abated.'

Another face appeared above Darcy and this time she knew every feature, every shading of skin and hair, and the way the tawny eyes could mute their alertness to a slumbrous half-smile.

'How do you feel, little one?' His voice brushed deep and soft across her most sensitive nerves, and the lamplight caught in his lashes and cast their shadows on the fine, hard angles of his face. Languid as she felt, Darcy wanted to raise her hand and touch him ... she was still alive and it had been Julio's swift actions which had saved her. Far down in her leg she felt the throbbing wound where without hesitation he had cut her in order to drain the venom.

'I—I can feel that I'm still alive.' She managed to

smile, though the frailty of her own voice came as
rather a shock. 'Thanks to you——'

With an expressive movement of his hand he waved
aside her thanks. 'It happens sometimes down in the
wine valley, one of the workers is bitten and it becomes
second nature to react quickly. What I can't understand
is how the snake came to be in your room; the staff
are always told to keep a watchful eye in case one
should slither in from the patios and hide in a dark
corner. Carlos found it beneath your bed and promptly
despatched it.'

Darcy gave a shiver and was propped up by the nurse
so she might drink some cool fruit juice through a
straw. It was deliciously soothing, just as the sight
of Julio was, seated on the edge of her bed, on the
side where her uninjured foot curled its toes at his
nearness. She couldn't fight her reaction to him in her
normal state, let alone right now. Her senses fed on
the look of him, big and sensuously dark in the brown
shirt which blended with his skin.

'The thing petrified me,' she said huskily. 'I was
standing by the window looking at the moon——'

'The window!' He snapped his fingers. 'It was open,
eh? The English must have their breath of air and you
opened it to the night?'

'Yes——' Darcy bit her lip. 'Just an inch or so—you
mean it squeezed in through that little gap?'

'It would seem so, *niña*.' He closed his warm fingers
around her hand. 'Our region is semi-tropical and our
wild things are not so innocuous as your English kind.
It's better not to invite them in of a night.'

The image of the snake glided through her mind, its
prong of a tongue weaving in and out as it focused
on her and struck. As her body recoiled from the

memory she wanted to throw her arms around Julio and cling close to him, sheltered from the things that could frighten and hurt. She looked at him and he was gazing back at her, his black brows meshed in a frown above the straight line of his Latin nose.

'You must push it from your mind,' he ordered. 'You are out of danger and there will only be a small scar just above your ankle. You can live with that, eh?'

'Of course.' She dragged her gaze from his and glanced around her room, seeing that it was night time. 'Will I be well enough to—to be married in the morning?'

'You were to have been married yesterday morning.' Julio leaned forward as she turned startled eyes to his face. 'You passed out cold when I had to cut you and then became delirious for a while, afterwards falling into a deep sleep. A whole day has passed—the wedding had to be cancelled.'

'Oh!' Her heart gave a throb of such relief that she had to sink back against her pillows in order to catch her breath. The day she had dreaded to live through— her wedding day—had been spent while she slept off the effects of the snakebite. She lay in the protective shadow of Julio's shoulders and knew he was reading her eyes and what they couldn't shield from him.

'I wonder why you couldn't run away when you saw the snake?' His eyes were thoughtfully narrowed as he turned to the nurse. 'Could you go and tell my brother that this young woman is now awake and will probably eat an omelette in a short while?'

'*Si, señor.*' With a rustle of starched skirts the nurse left the room and quietly closed the door behind her.

Darcy rested against her pillows, but beneath the covers her heart was beating excitedly. Being alone with Julio was intoxicating, giving her that feeling of being in danger and being protected as he took in her hair, tousled and fair in the lamplight, and the shell-pink chiffon against her bare arms. His look of strength made her feel extra fragile, and the fact that he had left his knife mark on her body was somehow erotic.

'God help me, what have I forced you into?' With a groan he buried his lips in the palm of her hand. 'You know what I've done, don't you? I've ruined your life and my own!'

'You saved my life, Julio——' She could feel the sensuous heat of his mouth against her skin and she wanted to reach out and touch his black hair, stroke it down into his nape and have his warm mouth buried against the fast beating of her heart.

'Saved it for Ramon,' he said thickly. 'You still have to go through with your marriage to him—how can it be otherwise? He clings to you—I long for you in ways he can't fulfil. I engineered a rack for both of us when I ordered you to marry him, and now there's no way to stop the torment from going on. We have to endure it. We can't cripple him yet again, *mi amada*, just because we long to be in each other's arms.'

'Oh, Julio!' It was a cry from her heart, the brief joy extinguished as she gazed at his dark head bent over her hand and realised that he meant every word he said to her.

He wanted her ... but that wasn't going to stop him from giving her in marriage to his brother.

'I can't see Ramon crippled again.' He towered to his feet in the lamplight and following the movement Darcy saw the resolve hardening in his eyes. 'I have to make you go through with it—I have to!'

The cut of his words went deeper than the cut in her flesh, as if he forced a blade through the very nerve centres of her body. He was a Spaniard and honour came before a woman. Those lean, dark, clenching hands at his sides might want possession of her, but he had to give her to Ramon and she had to let him do it.

'When?' The word was a thread of sound and she could feel herself shrinking away from the answer.

'A week,' he said. 'You'll be given time to recover your strength.'

'I—I might leave my window open again——'

'You dare!' He leaned over her, his face dark with sudden passion. 'It's enough to bear that I have to let another man have you—how do you think I feel?'

'If you hurt as much as I do, Julio, then it's some compensation.'

His features twisted as if a whip flicked across them and his fingers gripped the lace-edged pillow. Silently they regarded each other, and then as if driven he brought his mouth down hard against hers and kissed her until her arms were straining around him and there was nothing but the desperation of their embrace ... no awareness of anyone but themselves.

When someone entered the bedroom they were too lost in themselves to hear the shocked exclamation the sight of them brought forth. Julio was almost covering Darcy, who lay on her pillows so her face and neck were bared for his mouth. One of her arms was locked about his body, while the fingers of her left hand caressed the nape of his neck. They were totally abandoned to each other, black hair mingling with pale skin as his mouth travelled down into the division of the shell-pink nightdress.

'Julio!' The sound of his name echoed like a broken note shattering their sweet wild harmony. They broke apart in confusion and guilt, Darcy's hand instantly flying to the neck of her disarrayed nightdress, while

Julio fought to compose his face as he straightened up and brushed the black hair from his brow. Tiny beads of sweat had broken out along his upper lip and a nerve was pulsing there. His eyes flickered between his lashes and he looked as if he could have killed the intruder.

CHAPTER EIGHT

'Julio!' His aunt stood just inside the room holding a tray in her hands and there was an outraged look on her face. '*Dios mío*, am I to believe my own eyes? A nephew of mine to behave in such a way!'

'You are not to have hysterics, *amita*.' He strode to her. 'Please give me the tray before you drop the contents all over the carpet.'

Doña Ansonia gazed at him as if he had become a stranger to her. 'Julio, what has that girl done to you?'

'The blame is entirely mine.' He took the tray from her unsteady hands. 'Darcy has done nothing wrong——'

'You think me a fool, nephew? To come in here and find Ramon's *novia* in your arms—such disgraceful behaviour! Has neither of you any shame?'

'I tell you Darcy is blameless.' He spoke with an edge to his voice. 'Whatever happened was not with her consent, you understand me? I took advantage of her and she was too weak to hold me off.'

'I noticed she was holding you!' His aunt glanced past him to where Darcy lay as he had left her, curled up as if to hide herself, a hand crushed against her mouth, the pupils of her eyes hugely dark, nerves flinching at the way Doña Ansonia swept scornful eyes over her.

'I'm not to be palmed off with that story, Julio. I've

seen your eyes on the girl more than once, when you've thought yourself unobserved, and I know what Spanish men can be like when a fancy for a woman takes hold of them. You should be married, with a woman of your own to keep you from lusting after what belongs to Ramon. Isn't it enough that you have Dorina panting for you?'

'Aunt, you will close those doors and keep your voice lowered! We don't want the entire household to hear your accusations——'

'Accusations?' She flung out her hands dramatically. 'Are you trying to pretend that I'm inventing what I saw going on in that bed?'

'Only one of us was in the bed,' he snapped. He brought the tray to the bed table and placed it there, casting a rather grim look at Darcy. 'The poor child has been through a trying experience and I was consoling her. I mean nothing to her and she will tell you so. She was upset and in pain from her ankle—come, Darcy, repeat to my aunt what you have called me on more than one occasion. Arrogant, high-handed, with none of my brother's boyish charm.'

Darcy ran the tip of her tongue around her lips, still sensitive from the feel of his. She knew that for Ramon's sake she must agree that Julio had kissed her against her will, but she didn't know how she was going to say the words when her body still clamoured for him.

'What's in a kiss?' Her voice sounded strange, as if her real self refused to say these things. 'We do it all the time in my country, in cafeterias, on railway platforms, at bus stops. Is a kiss reckoned so important here in Spain?'

As she spoke the flippant words Darcy saw Julio half-close his eyes and she knew he was remembering the hunger of her mouth meeting his, the clasp of her arms holding him to her, the leap of her heart when he touched her.

His aunt had called it lust ... perhaps it was. A Spaniard attracted to the alien fairness of her skin and hair ... someone English drawn to his dark supple strength. An attraction of opposites. Dawn and dusk reaching impossibly for each other.

'When you are married,' replied his aunt, 'it's most important that you kiss no other man but your husband. I'm not without a spark of understanding, young woman. It would be unnatural if you didn't look at Julio and see him as other women see him. He has no right to be still unmarried, and I have said this to him often enough. He has his obligations to the estate, and he has his own natural inclinations, but he knows very well that he has no right to feel them where you are concerned. You are Ramon's *novia* and as much bound to him as if the priest had already sealed the knot. Do I make myself clear?'

'It won't happen again, aunt.' It was Julio who spoke, his voice firm and hard. 'Darcy wanted a little comfort, that was all, and had Ramon been able to supply it, you wouldn't have entered this room and found his young woman in my arms.'

'That,' murmured his aunt, 'is the problem, is it not, Julio? Your poor dear brother can't supply what this young woman appears to have need of.'

'*Amiga*,' he gave a curt laugh, 'how you dramatise the situation! Darcy had been bitten by a snake and was still feeling nervous. I kissed her. Is that a crime?'

'It might have turned into one had I not entered the room when I did.' Doña Ansonia frowned and looked him up and down. 'Your *machismo* is a little too much, and if you take my advice you'll announce your engagement to Dorina at the wedding of your brother. It would be a good idea, eh? A wife of your own might keep this girl out of your clutches.'

Darcy lay there with her heart pleading that he would dismiss his aunt's suggestion, but he didn't move or speak, he stood there tall and broodingly thoughtful, the brown shirt open against the chest where his heart remained a mystery to Darcy. Her eyes slid to his hands, partly clenched against the sides of his fawn trousers. Those brown, strong, horseman's hands would never clutch a woman ... it was unendurable for Darcy that they might fondle Dorina in the intimacy of marriage.

Her heart jolted as his tawny eyes met hers and held them. 'I shall think about it,' he said deliberately. 'I'm well aware that my obligations to the Valdez name come before anything else—that's the way it has been for eighteen years, since I took over the running of the place and swore to make it the finest estate in Andalusia. Have I ever veered from that course, *amiga*? Have I ever given anyone cause to doubt my word, my intentions, my affection for my family?'

'Never.' Doña Ansonia reached out and touched him with possessive fingers, her glance moving from his face to Darcy. 'A true Spaniard puts honour and family before flights of fancy. You are Spanish, Julio, and will obey the dictates of your conscience.'

He inclined his head, but there in the blackness of his hair, in the darkness of his skin, in the tawny alertness of his eyes, were the signs of another heritage ... that of the savage horsemen who had come riding into Spain, the sands of the desert still clinging to their robes. They had followed the dictates of their blood, and that blood was running warm and strong in Julio's veins.

'You must eat your supper before it gets cold,' he said to Darcy. 'You must eat and get strong again.'

'Yes,' said his aunt. 'We don't want to disappoint Ramon a second time.'

Darcy made no protest ... nothing mattered if Julio was going to marry Dorina, and he had just said that he would think about it. He was the head of the Valdez family and he had worked too hard to restore the valley to cast it all aside for the sake of passion. He would find ample passion with Dorina; that had been demonstrated while they danced.

Darcy allowed her pillows to be banked behind her shoulders and when her tray was uncovered she began to eat the fluffy omelette, hardly aware of its delicious taste, for all her senses were concentrated upon Julio, pausing at her threshold to light a cigarrillo before leaving her bedroom.

'Aunt,' he said, his eyes narrowed against the smoke, 'what you saw in this room was of no consequence and you will be good enough not to speak of it to anyone. You understand me?'

'I understand, Julio, if I have your solemn promise that Ramon isn't made to suffer because you find his *novia* a source of attraction. You have all your faculties and can go seeking your unimportant pleasures, as men will, but that poor boy——'

'Quite.' His nostrils tensed and his brows were drawn blackly together. 'Ramon is tied to that damned chair and I know it all too well. Do you think it doesn't twist my guts in a knot to see him like that? Do you imagine I would deliberately do anything to add to his suffering?'

'You were in here, nephew, with her.' Doña Ansonia flung out a ringed hand towards Darcy. 'She's a

foreigner and knows no better, but you—you a Valdez!
It came as a shock, I can tell you.'

'I tell you there was nothing to it,' he said grimly.
'Why do you women always have to imagine that a
kiss is significant? Nine times out of ten it's no more
than an impulse—like sneezing. The girl was upset
and her ankle is still painful. I had to inform her that
her wedding had to be cancelled.'

'By taking her in your arms and kissing her *in bed*?'
His aunt regarded him with the knowledge of her years
in her eyes. 'I'm not so ancient that all my fires are
dead, Julio. You are an *hombre macho* and I doubt if
any woman, young or old, could look at you without
a stirring in her veins, but all the same, *caro*, this girl is
almost your brother's wife and you would be wise to
remember it in future.'

'If you doubt my wisdom then you had best provide
her *with a dueña*,' he said dryly.

'I might do that,' replied his aunt. 'And I would advise you to provide yourself with a *novia*. Tonight
signifies that you are ready to marry!'

He bowed his head half-mockingly. 'Is this a polite
form a blackmail, *amiga*? I buy your silence in exchange for putting a gold bracelet on the wrist of your
daughter-in-law?'

Doña Ansonia gave a very Latin shrug. 'Why not,
Julio? Dorina is most certainly ripe for remarriage,
as was shown to all of us when she danced with you
the other evening. You know what we say in Spain?
When two people dance as one, so will they love.'

'Really?' He gave a slight rather grating laugh. 'I
once saw a pair of gipsies dance at a fair and it was an
extraordinary performance, then only a short while
after their flamenco the girl put a knife in the young

man and was hastened off to the local jail calling him every lecherous name she could think of.'

'You aren't a gipsy,' his aunt retorted, 'and neither is Dorina. She has all it takes to make you a good wife, Julio. Everyone is only waiting for you to say the word.'

'I suppose if I say that word, *amiga*, you will keep quiet about what you have witnessed tonight in this room?'

'*Seguramente.*'

'Spanish women can be ruthless.'

'When it's to the advantage of their families,' she agreed.

'Very well.' He didn't so much as glance in Darcy's direction. 'On the day of my brother's marriage I shall announce that I wish to pay court to Dorina. Everything should be done in the correct Spanish style, eh?'

'When people are correct, Julio, they don't get themselves into trouble.' Doña Ansonia was looking at Darcy as she spoke. 'How you peck at your food, girl! Have you no appetite for the omelette?'

Darcy knew what the Spanish woman implied ... she had seen with a pair of sharp eyes the hunger with which Darcy had wrapped her arms about Julio, holding him to her in that devouring kiss his aunt would hold at his head like a weapon. No one seeing them together would have believed that he was offering a little comfort to the invalid, and now that wild moment of indiscretion had to be paid for.

'Come.' Julio took his aunt by the arm. 'Let us leave Darcy alone.'

'See that you do that,' she rejoined.

For a brief moment as he closed the doors his eyes met Darcy's and he quirked an eyebrow, silently letting her know that for now they must allow his aunt to have the final word. The doors snapped shut and with a sigh Darcy laid aside her fork, certain that one more mouthful of omelette would choke her.

She replaced the tray on the bed table and lay back wearily against her pillows, the throbbing in her ankle keeping time with the throb of her heart. She wasn't certain if it was love she felt for Julio; she only knew that each time they were alone, each time they came in contact, a breathless kind of magic was in the air and nothing seemed to matter except that they surrender themselves to each other.

Her fingers stroked the embroidery of her pillow and still she seemed to feel the warm nape of his neck and to hear the catch in his breath when she pressed her fingertips into his nape, as if that part of him was rather sensitive. It intrigued her that any part of Julio should be sensitive when he looked so strong and assured. The aroma of him still clung to her nostrils, a combination of warm skin, soap and cigar smoke, and a dash of the Chivas Regal he liked to drink.

In all her life there had never been anyone like Julio and she wondered if she could be in love with him ... was love a sensation of need overlapped by waves of bittersweet pleasure?

She didn't doubt her resentment of Ramon. It had been growing in her and was now at a frightening peak .. the very idea of marrying him had become distasteful. He would want to touch her, and she crushed a hand against her mouth as if to stifle a cry. He couldn't be her lover in the fullest sense, but he would be able to caress and fondle her, and have the right to do so!

Hadn't Julio realised that?

Or didn't he truly care that his brother would have the intimate rights of a husband, to have her with him day and night, to watch her when she dressed and undressed? A sense of numbing despair swept over her that she must submit to all this, her body used by Ramon to give him what ease and comfort he could find in his state of half-being.

She had to go through with it, Julio had said so. She had to marry Ramon and by doing so become a sister to a man who aroused in her feelings that could never be sisterly. It would be a kind of incest when each time she looked at him she felt her body ache and yearn and grow weak with the desire to be locked in his arms. It would be hell when each time Ramon touched her, she longed instead for the tough, strong hands of his brother on her body, their hardness on her skin arousing her to a sharply sweet, almost desperate delight.

She groaned and turned about restlessly in her bed ... it would surely be a greater sin to marry Ramon than to tell him honestly that she didn't love him and couldn't live with him?

Yet ... yet if she did tell him the truth, Julio would turn against her and never again in this life would she feel his lips mating with hers, never again feel his arms closing warm around her, holding her so she was aware of every vibrant part of him.

Either way she felt trapped. Married to Ramon she would be forbidden to Julio, and if she told Ramon she couldn't marry him, he'd be so shattered that Julio would hate her!

She couldn't bear it again, to be treated with scorn and dislike by him. Not so long ago he had sat on the side of her bed and called her 'little one' and the endearment had melted her deep down inside herself. She wanted to please him, to do everything that would ignite those soft lights in his eyes ...

Oh God—her fingers clenched the linen of her pillow. If she wanted to keep some part of Julio and not be thrown irredeemably out of his life, then she had to go through with her marriage to Ramon and not shatter the last remnants of his pride by jilting him. Julio would never forgive her for that, and she flinched from an image of him bitterly telling her to get out of his sight before he made a cripple of her.

Only moments after breathless kisses that made the room spin round he had said that she must marry Ramon, and Darcy now lay very still and faced the realisation that his desire for her was less than his brotherly love for Ramon, whom he had cared for all his life. He was still determined to help his crippled brother feel more of a man by having a woman of his own. There were plenty of other women for Julio to hold in his arms. There was Dorina, who made no secret of her feelings. She'd be overjoyed to marry the virile master of San Solito, not only for the prestige of the position, but for the man himself.

Darcy lay silent and bleak as she visualised her future life in this house. Her own marriage would be without the joy of two people who found physical and mental stimulation in each other's company. It would be a kind of servitude, and living under the same roof as Julio would be hell and heaven combined. If he became Dorina's husband there would be the additional torment of knowing that when they retired for the night the Spanish girl would lie in his arms, receive his kisses and be part of him in the passionate dark of the night.

A pain drove through Darcy that made her cry out. She sat up in bed, clasping her arms about herself and rocking to and fro as if to soothe the ache in her body.

She couldn't pretend to herself any more. She was in love with Julio ... madly, desperately, to such an extent that she was ready to face the torturing future rather than be sent away from him. Prepared to sacrifice

herself to Ramon, and to bear it if Dorina became
Julio's wife and began in a while to show signs of being
with his child.

The pain drove deep, twisting into Darcy, penetrating to the vulnerable core of her. She would give
her soul to be in Dorina's shoes, free to entice him, and
to have with him the passionate fulfilment that would
make a child in his image, black of hair, with eyes like
slithers of gold, and a tawny skin that rippled to his
supple movements. Darcy shivered and yet she felt
hot. She was unaware that someone had entered her
bedroom until she felt a cool hand pressed to her forehead.

'You are in distress, señorita?'

Darcy gazed up at the nurse and her eyes spoke for
her.

'I will give you a sedative and that should make you
sleep. It is your ankle that troubles you? You would
like me to take a look to ensure there is no infection?'

Darcy complied, for it seemed as if such pain had to
have a source ... love couldn't be so terrible that it
did this to one's body and made it feel as if it were
bruised all over.

The nurse drew the bedcovers to one side and took a
careful look at the wound beneath a strip of dressing.
'This is beginning to heal, señorita. I see no sign of
infection and can't understand why you say it hurts.'

'It's probably my imagination.' Darcy managed a
slight smile. 'Will I be allowed out of bed tomorrow?
I do hope so.'

'We shall see.' The skilled fingers applied a fresh
dressing and the covers were smoothed. 'There will be
only a small scar on your leg, but such occurrences
play on the mind and you must try as soon as possible
to put it out of your mind. There will be your wedding

to think about, eh? You must love the Señor Valdez very much, *señorita*.'

'You mean because he's an invalid?'

The nurse shrugged slightly and ran her eyes over Darcy, who with her fair hair dipping on her forehead above faintly shadowed eyes looked very young and vulnerable, as if she needed taking care of herself. Only love could make such a responsibility worth taking on, otherwise the burden might become hard to bear after a time. The *señor* is very good-looking, of course, and must have been a young man difficult to resist when you first knew him.'

Yet Darcy had resisted him ... it had been Julio who had made such an overwhelming impact on her defences. It was for love of him that she was taking on the responsibility of Ramon, and there was a tinge of cynicism in her smile.

'There seems to be something in a woman's nature that allows love to make a fool of her. Do you think I'm unwise, nurse, to marry a man in a wheelchair?'

'I wouldn't wish it for a daughter of mine,' the woman replied. 'Has it ever been suggested that the *señor* might recover one of these days?'

Darcy shook her head. 'It seems unlikely. His brother has had him examined by some of the leading specialists in the field of paraplegia and they haven't been too hopeful. Have you known of any cases which have made a recovery?'

'It happens occasionally that the nerves in the spinal column make a spontaneous return to their normal state and sensation gradually returns to the patient. It can be the effects of severe shock which bring about the paralysis ... as it can sometimes be the result of another shock which induces the cure. But I don't wish to raise your hopes, it is perhaps best to accept the word of the specialists. If they feel that the condition is likely to be permanent, then I expect they are right. It's a pity that your own life will be affected—you are young, normal, and bound to contrast your husband with his brother.'

Darcy's heart gave a nervous leap. 'Please don't say that——!'

The nurse shrugged and moved her hands in a Latin gesture. 'That one has the *machismo*, as we say. He catches the eye of women and turns their thoughts to *amor*, no matter what age they might be. Some Spaniards are like that, and I say again that you are a young woman. It is natural for any woman to want what a man can give her.'

A feeling of heat came over Darcy and she felt it burning high on her cheeks. Was everyone going to guess that behind her polite attentions to Ramon there lay a wild yearning for the *dueño* to throw her across a bed and make her glad to be a woman?

'As I say,' the nurse picked up the tray, 'I would be very reluctant to see a daughter of mine entering into a marriage that couldn't fulfil her or give her children. Such a man has to become the child and the woman hasn't a husband in the true sense of the word. Are your own parents happy for you, *señorita*?'

'I have only a mother and she lives far away. I'm of an age to please myself what I do with my life.'

'By becoming nursemaid to a young man who is partially helpless, eh?' The nurse shook her head in doubt. 'He's rich, of course, but money isn't everything.'

'I'm not marrying Ramon for his money,' Darcy said indignantly. 'Is that what people will think?'

'They are bound to, eh? You are a pretty girl, and I have worked in enough city clinics to have seen the ark roots of some of the so-called blondes. You had etter watch out for the brother if you do care for our young man.'

'Oh, go away!' Darcy smiled reluctantly. 'You're a ather wicked woman for a nurse and I shouldn't listen o you.'

'You are very young, *chica*, and I feel rather sorry or you. Now will you have a cup of hot chocolate to elp you sleep, or a sedative?'

'Hot chocolate, please, with just a dash of cinnamon.'

'Of course with cinnamon.' The Latin eyes twinkled. thought, somehow, that you liked the dash of spice. said it to myself when I saw the two of you to- ether——'

'Nurse!'

A finger was laid against the side of the nurse's nose nd tapped significantly. 'We see too much, and in a ickroom people are more likely to give themselves way. I will say this to you, English Miss, you are *loca* f you marry someone because you feel sorry for them.'

'It—isn't altogether that.' Darcy felt a twist of pain t what she faced from Julio if she jilted Ramon. 'I vas partly to blame for the accident in which Ramon vas hurt and I owe him—him and his family. You panish people have an unyielding sense of honour, aven't you?'

'Very true,' the nurse admitted, a thoughtful look n her eyes as she regarded Darcy. 'The tall one, he has his like iron in his spine, eh?'

Darcy nodded.

'I will fetch the hot chocolate—do you need assist- nce to the bathroom?'

'No, I can manage.'

There in the adjoining bathroom Darcy made her- elf more at ease and still felt rather shaky as she washed her face and hands. The mirror gave back her pensive, pale looks as she combed her hair. She must in future make sure that she and Julio were never alone. It was dangerous in more ways than one, for other people were beginning to sense that their regard for each other wasn't the innocent one it should be. It would be disastrous if Dorina ever found them alone together. Out of sheer malice she would go running to Ramon, and it would be awful if he had to learn from her that his fiancée and his brother ...

Darcy stared at herself in the mirror. The nurse had said that severe shock could induce paralysis ... and cure it!

But no ... not that way. Darcy backed away from the mirror and the desperation in her eyes. Ramon had been examined by the best doctors money could afford and each one had agreed that his condition was unlikely to improve. A shock involving Julio and herself could only be a stab in the heart to him ... it might injure him physically, and Julio would never forgive himself if anything happened to Ramon for which he was directly to blame. He would never take his happiness at Ramon's expense and to punish himself he would put her out of his reach. Probably on a plane to South Africa!

Darcy wandered back into her bedroom, limping slightly because her ankle still felt rather stiff.

She was halfway to the bed when instinct made her glance towards the doors. Julio was standing there with his back to them, a circular tray in his hand holding a cup and saucer.

'No!' she gasped.

'It's all right,' he said. 'I persuaded the nurse to let me bring your chocolate drink.'

'Oh, you shouldn't be here——' Weakness overcame

Darcy and she sank down on the bed. 'Leave it and go!'

But he came to her, taking long steps across the carpet. He placed the tray on the table and leaned over her. 'I was concerned for you, *niña*. I had to see you— I know it came as a jolt for us to be caught by my aunt in such a compromising way. I wanted to assure you that she won't mention to anyone, least of all Ramon——'

'Ramon—Ramon,' Darcy took him up. 'That's all I hear! Ramon must come first and to hell with my feelings! I can tuck them out of sight, forget I have them. Play the devoted little wife while my stomach ties itself in knots each time I see you!'

Darcy gazed up stricken at Julio. 'Now—now you know, don't you?' she said weakly.

'I know you wouldn't kiss me unless you felt something for me——'

'Something?' She gave an off-key laugh. 'It was all music for me until there was you. Insulting me, ordering me to play up to Ramon and look happy about it, but none of that was enough for you, Julio, you had to go and make a fool of me with your renowned *machismo*. I-I'll marry your brother, but for God's sake leave me alone!'

'I knew it,' he murmured, 'you are upset and miserable, and you're trembling. Come, let me put you into your bed——'

As he reached for her Darcy slapped his hand away. 'Don't touch me,' she said tensely. 'You know that when you touch me I—I turn into a fool, and it can't be like that or I shall go crazy! Go away! Go and find Dorina and leave me in peace!'

Julio didn't move, he gazed down intently at her, his eyes narrowing when a convulsive shiver ran over her.

'I can't leave you like this,' he said, his voice equally tense. 'If I call the nurse she'll pump you with some drug that will make you feel high, and then low in the morning. I'm going to stay with you for a while!'

'No,' Darcy shook her head wearily. 'It's too dangerous—I promise you I shall be all right. Y-you make me nervous——'

'I think you need me.' He spoke decisively and strode over to the doors. 'There should be a key so these can be locked, but it appears to be missing. I'll fix one of these chairs under the handles.'

Darcy watched dumbly as he proceeded to secure the doors, her eyes fixed wide and rather frightened upon his face as he came back to her. 'Julio, you can't stay——'

'I can't leave you all strung up and shaking with nerves, *carina*. Right now you need a shoulder to lean on—mine.'

'There'd be such a scandal,' she breathed. 'You know how your aunt reacted earlier on—please be sensible, Julio.'

'I'm not going to make love to you.' He handed her the cup of chocolate. 'Drink this before it gets cold—mind, don't spill it over the bed. Shall I hold it for you so you can sip from it like a little girl?'

'I—I'm not a little girl——' A sudden wave of colour ran over her skin as she caught the glint of confirmation in his eyes. There was a tremor in her hands as she held the cup and drank from it, every nerve, every fraction of her skin aware of him in a lounging position on her bed. He casually kicked off his shoes and as they fell to the carpet her heart missed a beat. He looked incredibly dark and big against the pale bedcovers, watching her, waiting for her to finish the chocolate ...

'It's all right,' he murmured, his smile quizzical. 'My intentions are entirely noble. I'm going to stay with you until you fall asleep, and I bet it's been years since someone rocked you off to dreamland.'

'This will turn into a nightmare if we're caught, Julio.'

'I'll hide in the wardrobe if anyone tries the door.' His eyes were glimmering as he reached for her and drew her deeply into his arms. 'Pretend I'm your papa.'

'Some hopes of that!' She allowed her head to sink down upon his warm shoulder but her body wouldn't relax. Her ears were straining for the slightest sound on the gallery and unaware her fingers were gripping his upper arm until she was pinching him with her fingernails.

'You'll draw blood in a moment,' he murmured.

'Oh—forgive me!' Her eyes met his and she quickly pulled her hand away. 'I'm so on edge and I do think it would be best if you left me alone.'

'Turn the record over and relax.' Still holding her in one arm, he drew the bedcovers over her feet and legs. 'Right now, little one, I have no ulterior motive and have only your welfare on my mind. How long have you been on your own without a mother to care for you?'

'My mother remarried and went to live in South Africa when I was fifteen. I was away at school at that time, then after I left school I enrolled at the music academy a-and felt quite independent. I was really quite good at standing on my own two feet until——' Darcy bit her lip. 'The Valdez brothers have had a devastating effect on my life, one way and another.'

'If your mother had taken you to South Africa with her, we should not have met. Would you have preferred not to have known me, *niña*?'

Darcy lay pillowed against his shoulder, her eyes moving over the proud Spanish face with its traces of the east in his skin and the shape of his desert coloured eyes. Her emotions were torn in two ... it was exciting to love a man, if you were meant to love him, but everything between Julio and herself had to be clandestine, snatched behind closed doors, concealed from other people because she was committed to his brother.

'I—I think it might have been better for all concerned had we never met,' she replied. 'Had I gone to South Africa, Ramon wouldn't have been injured in my car, and we'd all be living our lives so differently. I know that Spaniards believe in fate, but it's been a very unkind one, hasn't it?'

'*Mal ángel*,' he agreed, winding her hair into a ring on her cheek. 'It stood dark at the crossroads and struck hard with its sword, literally cutting off Ramon at the legs. I wouldn't give a damn if he wasn't helpless. I would do more this moment than hold you in my arms!'

Darcy caught her breath at the look in his eyes, and she had to fight for composure, for the strength not to reach out and clasp her arms about his neck. She wanted to beg him to release her from Ramon, but she knew—oh God, she knew what his answer would be!

'Is there any hope that Ramon will ever regain the power to walk?' she asked quietly. 'Were the doctors so adamant?'

He inclined his head. 'We were told that if he didn't regain some of his former zest for living, his condition would grow worse. I could see that happening daily, and then he tried to end his life, as I told you. That was why I didn't oppose his wish to have you with him. I remembered you as a long-legged student protesting your right to see Ramon in hospital. I didn't regard you as a woman but as a flighty girl who had caused damage to my brother. I could have put my hands around your throat and choked the breath out of you—little did I dream that the next time I saw you I would want to kiss the breath out of you.'

'At the railway station?' Darcy gave a shaky smile. 'You seemed to me as brusque and domineering as ever, and I nearly passed out when you told me I had to marry Ramon.'

'Yes, you have to marry Ramon,' he agreed moodily. 'After tonight we shall never be alone like this again. I'm risking it right now because your nerves are shot to pieces and you need my care for a short while. Is the therapy having an effect?'

Oh yes, she thought, it was having quite an effect on her to be held in his arms, her lightly clad figure warmed by his closeness, the pressure of his forearm muscles making her feel secure and weak at one and the same time.

'I—I'm still on edge in case someone forces open the door,' she said. 'What on earth would we say——?'

'I'd say I was comforting you, and it would be the truth this time, would it not?'

Their eyes met and Darcy was made instantly aware of what would happen if their lips met. She saw a pulse beating as if tormented at the side of his brown neck ... warm strong neck she longed to touch with her lips.

'I—I think you had better go, Julio——' She made a faint-hearted attempt to withdraw from his arms, but he refused to release her, his eyes faintly smiling at her inability to escape from him ... he knew she didn't really want to and the awareness was alive and tingling between them.

'I'm staying until you fall asleep and I won't be denied the right to do so——'

'You have no rights,' she broke in, for it was the stark truth. 'Ramon has those, a-and even if he were with me at this hour of the night, your family would be shocked. Please, Julio, don't make things harder for me to bear!'

'You are pretending it isn't pleasant to be alone like this with me?'

'It's dangerous——'

'All life is dangerous, little one.' He ran a finger over the sensitive areas of her left ear and moved down the side of her neck in circling motions that sent whirlpools of feeling to the very centre of her body. Darcy had to force herself to remain tense when she felt a compulsion to move nearer to him, to press herself soft and yielding to his hardness. The very thought made her feel faint and of their own accord her eyes grew heavy and languid, half-closing the lids so the shadows of her lashes fell upon her skin.

She lay like that and knew he watched her. Let him think she was falling asleep when in reality she knew herself sensuously aroused by him. It would have been sheer bliss to surrender herself ... to forget everything in the sweet-wild realms of passion where nothing mattered beyond the moment.

'There,' he murmured, 'you grow drowsy and soon you will be asleep.'

'You'll leave then, Julio—promise?'

'You know I never break my promises, *niña*.'

No, she thought. The promise he had made Ramon was unbreakable, and it was she who was torn between the two men, her body mad for Julio, and her conscience all she had to give the man who was going to be her husband. It wasn't enough but it was all she had to give, the rest of her cleaved to the strength, the dash of arrogance, the Iberian gallantry that made Julio the man he was ... a man capable of handing her over to someone else in the certain knowledge that her happiness would be blighted, that never could she be fulfilled emotionally or physically and would lead a robot existence with not even a child to compensate her.

Darcy should have hated him, but all she knew as she lay in his arms was that he filled her with hopeless love and longing. The only way to escape from the torment was to give in to her spent emotions and fall asleep. He would leave her then. Slip away from her side and be in the morning the tall, courtly *dueño* he always appeared in front of his family. Only his aunt would have her suspicions, and Darcy felt sure that from now on Doña Ansonia would keep a strict eye on both of them.

Yes, she must fall asleep and then Julio would go quietly from her bedroom and no one would be any the wiser that he had been here, sharing her bed.

Her eyes closed and with an inarticulate little murmur Darcy drifted off into the warm depths of sleep, her fair hair spread across the brown skin of Julio's throat.

He made no movement that might have disturbed her ... his arms stayed wrapped around her body in the shell-pink nightdress.

CHAPTER NINE

Darcy woke abruptly, expecting to find herself alone. Her heart nearly stopped when she felt the slack weight of an arm across her body and felt breathing movements close to her.

Julio ... he hadn't gone as he'd promised but lay soundly asleep at her side.

She gazed at him, half terrified to see him there, and yet also deeply fascinated as she studied his unaware face, with its shading of morning beard, and the dense lashes lying very still and concealing the eyes that could be so disturbing when he was awake. Darcy's breath quickened. It was alarming and exciting to be so intimately close to him, but sunlight was slipping through the windows and she must awaken him. Very carefully she reached out a hand and gently brushed the black hair back off his forehead; he stirred, grumbled a little in his sleep and then moved closer still to her until his bristly face was against her skin.

She quivered at the feel of him and felt a warm, melting sensation deep in her body. She wanted these precious, clandestine moments never to end ... she wished the world could be shut outside those bedroom doors, and that here inside this room Julio and herself had every right to be alone. If they had such rights she could awaken him with kisses and there would be no one to call it wrong if he didn't leave this room until noon.

As it was ... Darcy reached out to shake his shoulder, but her hand was arrested by the sudden rattling of the door handle. She stared across the room petrified, for the chair under the handle was beginning to move as pressure was exerted on the double doors.

No! The word moved soundlessly on her lips. Go away ... leave us alone, we've done nothing wrong!

The chair fell with a thud and Julio sat up with a startled oath on his lips.

Dorina stood there in her riding outfit, a whip clenched in her hand. Her dark eyes blazed at the two of them, taking in Darcy's tousled fair hair and the lacy band of her nightdress half off her shoulder. Her gaze moved like a flick of her whip to Julio, raking over him and taking in the obvious fact that he had slept with Darcy.

A spate of Spanish broke from her lips, spoken so rapidly and furiously that Darcy couldn't follow it ... until one word spoken with venom couldn't help but catch her attention.

Puta—harlot!

'That is enough!' Julio sprang from the bed with the agility and danger of a cougar. He took long strides across the room and caught Dorina by the wrist, wrenching away the whip she had raised to strike him. 'Call me every offensive name you can crowd on your tongue, but leave Darcy alone. Whatever you think has taken place in this room is no more than an illusion, but I have no way to convince you of it except to say that if you call this child by that name one more time, I shall slap it from your hysterical mouth. You will listen to me——'

'And hear some more about illusions?' Dorina

wrenched herself away from him and stood with her breast heaving under her riding jacket. 'I knew from the moment that milk-skinned little mare came into this house that you'd be after her—like one of your own Arab stallions? What was it like, eh? Was she sweet and docile when you——'

'Shut your slut's mouth!' He swung his hand and it was only a cry of protest from Darcy that made him strike the air instead of Dorina's face. Hastily she ran out of the room, calling back over her shoulder: 'Ramon is going to be told about this! He should be informed that he's taking for a bride his brother's *puta*!'

Julio sprang to the door, a hand gripping the framework as he hung there in a kind of agony. 'By the devil, she'll do it, Darcy! She'll tell him I have been with you all night, and who is going to believe that I didn't do what she implied?'

Darcy knelt up on the bed and gazed at him in a stricken silence. '*Mala suerte*, no?' He strode up and down, striking the air with the furled whip. 'All I wanted was to be with you for a while, then like a fool I had to fall asleep by your side. *Por Dios*, to hear of this might kill Ramon and I shall be like Cain, eh?'

He came to the bedside and gazed broodingly at Darcy. 'You are in no way to blame, *mi amada*. I should have remembered that Dorina has a tendency to snoop, and now I have to do what I can to convince Ramon that your sweet innocence is unsullied. When you think of it we might as well have been hung for a lamb as an illusion, eh?'

'You can't think Ramon is going to believe you?' Darcy gazed up at him, the fair hair tumbling about her brow, her mouth quivering above the tiny hollow in her chin. She saw the emotion go twisting across his face, reaching down into him until he gave a groan. He shook his head.

'We are Spaniards, Ramon and I. Had this happened to me, that my *novia* was found in bed with another man, then I would be unlikely to believe that nothing took place. You know why Dorina was so enraged? It's because you look adorable first thing in the morning, sweet as warm bread that a man would like to bite. She made it sound ugly, but I am like one of my own Arab stallions when I look at you, Darcy, and that is the truth. Even at this moment when I know trouble is brewing I should like to——'

With an oath he swung away from her, striking at the side of his thigh with the whip. 'What kind of a man am I? I have wanted women and I've had them, but it's blasphemy to lust after a girl who belongs to my own brother. God in heaven, what have I done to Ramon? I meant only to provide him with a little happiness, some joy in living, and now my self-indulgence of last night may cost him his very life.'

'Julio, you mustn't blame yourself.' Darcy slid from the bed and limped to his side. 'I should have insisted last night that you leave my room. I shouldn't have given in to my own longing—oh God, it is a mess, isn't it? Dorina's in love with you——'

'She fancied herself as mistress of San Solito,' he corrected. 'As my wife she would have the power to order people about—do you imagine I would ever give her that?'

'But you said—you agreed with your aunt that you'd marry Dorina.' Darcy gave him a bewildered look. 'Didn't you mean it, Julio?'

'As if I would!' His smile was brief and ironical. 'My

aunt is easier to deal with than her daughter-in-law, I fear. I merely said it to keep Doña Ansonia from guessing how I feel about you.'

'How do you feel about me, Julio?' Darcy felt that anything could be borne if he admitted just once that he loved her.

He gazed down at her, his eyes moving over her hair, her face, and her body.

'You are entirely feminine, Darcy,' he said, his gaze lingering on her bare left shoulder where the band of lace had slipped. 'You know the reaction you have on my masculinity. You appeal to the animal in me.'

Darcy couldn't suppress a hurt little cry at the way he said it, and the way he looked, a sudden insolence about him as he thrust the black hair from his brow.

'I see,' she said huskily. 'I suppose last night the animal in you was in one of its tame moods?'

'Exactly so.' He swung towards the doors which still gaped open and bending down he righted the chair which Dorina had knocked over in her determination to enter the room. 'I have to see Ramon. I have to try and explain my presence here with you. I wish I felt confident of making him believe the truth, but I fear he's more likely to believe Dorina's version of what happened last night. Be prepared for anything, Darcy.'

'W-what exactly does that mean?' She was standing very straight, her head poised so he wouldn't guess how bowed down she felt right now.

'He may demand that you be sent away from the *rancho*.' Julio stood very tall between the open doors, the riding whip very still in his hand. 'If Ramon asks for this, then I shall see to it. I must put my brother first.'

'Of course,' she said. 'What's a woman who only appeals to the animal side of a man?'

He shrugged his wide shoulders and was about to leave the room when she reminded him that he was leaving his shoes behind. 'I'll fetch them for you, Julio. I wouldn't want a reminder of you left behind.'

'*Gracias.*' He took the shoes but didn't bother to put them on. 'I can only offer my regrets for what has happened, Darcy. Have your breakfast here in your room. I'll get word to you later on about what is to become of you.'

'That's good of you, *señor*. A woman likes to know what is to become of her after a man has done with her.'

His shoulders tautened under the brown silk of his shirt, creased here and there from his night in her bed. 'Until later,' he said, and closed the bedroom doors behind him.

Darcy sagged physically and felt a wave of despair sweep over her. The print of Julio's arms was still around her, but her heart felt abandoned. He had gone to Ramon ... it was always his brother who had first call on his attention and his consideration, and she was left alone to feel like a—a scarlet woman.

She hated the feeling and wanted to wash away in a hot bath the guilt that lingered. Even if she and Julio hadn't made love, the intention and the desire had been there when Dorina had broken in upon them and found them together in bed. They had woken warm and close to each other, and Darcy couldn't hide from herself the knowledge that she would have given herself to Julio had they been left alone another few moments.

A tide of scarlet swept over her body, and dragging off her nightdress she hurried into the bathroom and stepped beneath the shower, turning the tap so the water pummelled her burning limbs. So this was what love did to a woman? It centred her entire thought and feeling upon one man, and made her shameless in her desires. No part of her belonged to herself any more; it was as if her body, her mouth, her hair were held in a kind of trust for him alone. Aching, tingling at the deepest roots for his utmost possession ... for her utmost surrender.

She squeezed the sponge tightly and soapy water ran down over her skin, wending its way over the curves which Julio had pressed to himself, half hurting them against his hardness. Darcy gave a tormented little groan. If Ramon no longer wished to marry her, then she'd be sent away from Julio. She didn't want to marry Ramon, but it was going to be unbearable never to see his tall, strong, demanding brother ever again. Everything inside her seemed to scream a protest, as if when the moment came to board the train away from him it would feel as if she were being pulled apart, leaving her heart with him as the train carried her away from San Solito, gathering speed until she saw the last of him on the platform.

It would happen! No one was going to believe that he'd slept in her bed without making love to her. He'd be forced to compromise her if he hoped to convince Ramon that he hadn't deliberately set out to betray him. Wasn't it always Delilah who beckoned the strong man and made him weak?

Darcy stepped on to the bathmat and draped a towel around her. She loved Julio, but to him she was just an inviting shape and smooth hair into which he had plunged his lean dark face, with those eyes that were the colour of the tameless desert.

Darcy was lost in thought as she dried herself, the steam fading from the big wall mirror and reflecting an image that was more charming than she knew. She told herself that the blame for last night would fall on her ... it would have to be that way if Julio hoped to convince Ramon that he could still trust him. He would have to make it look as if she, the English girl, had seduced him ... better for the outsider to be the culprit than the head of this Spanish household. She had never been wanted here, and now the family could endorse what Dorina had called her, and Ramon could be assured that he had had a lucky escape from a woman who couldn't be trusted with his own brother.

It was the ideal solution, Darcy told herself. At least she wouldn't have to marry a man she didn't love, but as she pushed back the damp hair from her brow she saw the bleakness in her eyes. Perhaps if Julio loved her, he would have done what other Spaniards did when caught in a risqué situation with a woman ... he would have said that they must marry, and their being together would have been excused as Iberian 'rape', a means by which a couple forced relatives to approve their union.

But Ramon came first with Julio. He would dismiss her from San Solito if that was what Ramon wanted ... he would turn his back on her rather than hurt his invalid brother by flaunting the fact that she preferred him, for it could only look as if she wanted a whole man in preference to one who couldn't make vital, natural love to her.

A painful tremor ran through Darcy. It was a situation that could tear Ramon's pride to ribbons, for how could she tell him that if Julio was stricken by polio, or if he lost his limbs in some awful accident, she would still love him and would want to do everything for him. Love made all the difference, and she had never felt that for Ramon. Love came unbidden, for she certainly hadn't asked of the fates that they plunge her into the turmoil of loving someone she couldn't have.

No way could she have Julio. He might desire her, but it wouldn't stop him from sending her away from San Solito in order to conciliate Ramon.

Darcy returned to the bedroom and was dressing when her nurse entered, carrying a breakfast tray. 'Ah, *señorita*, you have decided that you've had enough of bed. How are you feeling?'

Her manner was so normal when Darcy had been prepared for drama that she couldn't quite take it in. Surely Dorina had caused some sort of chaos downstairs, if she had carried out her threat to make trouble?

'I—I feel all right.' She smoothed her blouse and fastened her skirt. 'How is Señor Ramon?'

'As usual, I think.' The nurse bustled about laying out Darcy's breakfast on a table in front of the open balcony windows. 'It will please him, eh, that you have made such a good recovery? You must remember in future not to leave these windows open at night; during the daytime the hot sun keeps the pests in a sluggish mood, but they wake up when the sun goes down. Come, drink your coffee and eat this good food while it's hot.'

Darcy came to the table, her hair looped back at her nape, a look of perplexity in her eyes. She scanned the nurse's cheerful face but saw nothing there that gave any hint of the trouble and confusion Darcy had expected.

'Ah, before I forget.' The nurse slid a hand into a pocket of her uniform and withdrew an envelope. 'The Señor Julio asked me to give you this, *señorita*. He said something about some information you required.'

The pulse fluttered in Darcy's throat and it was with an effort that she took the envelope with a casual air. 'Thank you.' She laid it down beside her plate of poached eggs on toast, as if it were fairly unimportant and could wait for her attention. It looked as if Julio had done something to silence Dorina for a while, but what it was Darcy couldn't imagine. She longed to tear open the envelope which held his note, but instead she had to calmly sugar her coffee and make small talk with the nurse.

'Have you had your own breakfast, nurse?' she asked.

'Si, señorita.' A regretful looked crossed the woman's face. 'I am departing from the *rancho* very soon to go and attend another case. I shall miss looking after you. You have been a nice patient, as I told the Señor Julio. He is some *hombre*, that one! It would take a very cool woman not to be disturbed by such a man.'

Darcy could feel herself being studied as she sat there in a ray of sunlight and it took an effort to summon a composed smile in answer to the remark. It now seemed certain that if Dorina had carried out her threat to expose what she believed had taken place in this bedroom, the house would have been buzzing with the scandalous details and the nurse's manner would have been far from ordinary. Darcy's gaze dwelt on the sealed envelope and she had to control an urge to snatch it up, tear it open and discover why everything was quiet and calm when she had expected a storm.

'Don Julio is a gentleman,' she said. 'They're a dying breed in this world of ours, men who put others before themselves.'

'That is true.' The nurse inclined her capped head. 'It's called progress that the good old ways are dying out, and now it seems that only in these remote areas of Spain life continues with graciousness and the protection of the *dueños* of the old blood. It is useless to say that all men must be equal. There are those who are different, and it takes many years of breeding, as it takes time to breed fine horses.'

Darcy smiled and sipped her coffee, which was always delicious here at the *rancho*, made from beans that were roasted fresh each day. 'I think the *señor* would appreciate that sentiment, as a breeder of horses with an Arabian strain in them.'

'The strain is also in him, eh?' The nurse laid a finger against the side of her nose in a significant gesture. 'Well, I have to go and pack for my departure. I will see you in a while, *señorita*, to say goodbye and to wish you happiness in your marriage.'

Their eyes met, two women who really knew what lay in Darcy's heart. Impulsively the nurse reached out and briefly touched Darcy's hair. 'In this age of the self-seekers there are still those with the foolish heart, *la rubia. Vaya con Dios.*' With a rustle of starched skirts she left the room and as the doors closed behind her, Darcy reached for Julio's note. Her anxiety to read it was equalled by her apprehension and her hand was unsteady as she slit the envelope with the tip of a knife and withdrew the folded sheet of notepaper.

'*Carisima*,' it read, 'I am obliged after a discussion with Dorina to inform my family that she and I will be married very soon. She demands this in exchange for her silence and it's a price I have to pay for Ramon's sake. Instead of going to him, she awaited me in my room. When she left I saw the nurse bringing your breakfast and asked that she deliver this note to you. Destroy it now, *amiga*.'

Darcy rose from the table and tearing the notepaper and envelope into shreds, she then took them into the bathroom and flushed them away. Gone ... gone with every shred of hope that she and Julio might kiss again, somewhere, somehow.

Dorina had got her way, and for Ramon's sake Julio would marry her. It would please his family, but Darcy knew for certain that it would slowly destroy her if she had to live in the same house with the two of them. She went to the mirror and smoothed her hair, and after a little hesitation applied some blusher to her cheeks in order to hide their paleness. She had lost Julio and felt she had nothing else to lose ... she knew he would hate her after she had told Ramon that she could never marry him.

It was still quite early and the house was quiet as she made her way downstairs. She looked composed in her navy-blue blouse and pale pleated skirt, but her heart was hammering as she crossed the hall to the doors of Ramon's suite. She tapped on the door panel and could feel how nervously she was breathing, so that when Ramon's attendant came in answer to her knock she found herself stuttering.

'I—I wish to speak to—to Señor Ramon,' she said. 'Is he awake?'

'Si, señorita.' The man stepped to one side so she could enter the sitting-room of the suite. 'I was about to help him dress, but of course he will be only too pleased to see you.'

'Who is that?' Ramon called from the bedroom, and the next instant had wheeled his chair through the doorway. 'Darcy! Ah, what an unexpected pleasure! Have you come to comb my hair for me?'

That he looked so pleased to see her made her heart sink. It would have been so easy to go on lying to him; to go on pretending that she was his willing bride-to-be. All she had to do was to go across and kiss him and tell herself that somehow she would bear it, knowing that Julio's warm strong arms were holding to his hardness the willing body of another woman. A shudder swept her and she stood where she was, knowing she couldn't bear it.

Ramon was leaning forward in his chair, looking her intently up and down. '*Cómo estás la, chica?*'

'I'm quite well, Ramon. May we—talk?'

'*Muy bien.*' He glanced at his attendant. 'I shan't need you for a while, Gomez. Go and eat some food, eh?'

Gomez inclined his head, first at Ramon, then at Darcy, and the next moment had quietly left them alone. They gazed at each other, then abruptly Ramon held out a hand to her. 'Come and give me a kiss, eh? I have been concerned for you and Julio has had to provide me with bulletins. To think, *lindísima*, we should be man and wife by now if that snake hadn't struck you. It must have hurt, so come here and let me——'

'Ramon——' She stood where she was, her hands clenched at her sides, the fingernails digging into her palms as she gathered the courage to say the words that would strike the smile from his lean, slightly haggard but still handsome face. Thick black hair that was inclined to wave above his forehead, dark eyes that were entirely Latin, and a mouth with full and rather emotional lips. He had been so physically attractive before the accident that Darcy had never fully understood why she hadn't fallen helplessly in love with him. She had since learned that love was a strange, complex emotion, and that it struck a woman not in the eyes but in her innermost self, where it couldn't be torn out, a source of pain that could also provide intense pleasure. She had only to think of Julio and that living flame of love was melting her and it became unbearable that he wasn't there so the hot sweet melting could take place in his arms.

'I—I have something to say, Ramon, and I'm so afraid of—of hurting you——'

He stared at her, and then began to propel his chair towards her, closer all the time until she felt sure he was going to run her down rather than let her speak.

She stood still and didn't back away from him and he brought the wheelchair to a halt only inches from her legs. 'I'm used to being hurt,' he said. 'Living itself has become something that hurts, so go ahead and don't mind my feelings. I suppose you can't bring yourself to marry a cripple, is that it?'

Darcy shuddered visibly. 'It isn't just that, Ramon, believe me. I've tried so hard to—to love you, but marriage is becoming one with a man and I can't marry you. I'm sorry—so sorry!'

'Is there someone else?' The words struck at her, an edge to them, and she flinched as if she actually felt them. His eyes narrowed to dark steel and his body strained towards her. 'Tell me, I have the right to know! It can't be someone you knew in England, otherwise you wouldn't have come here with the intention of marrying me——'

'I didn't do that,' she broke in, and she was so white-faced with nerves that the blusher she had applied stood out against her skin like a hectic flush. 'I never came to San Solito with any such intention. I—I came to see you because I felt we were still friends and I wanted to see for myself that you were all right.'

'A proposal of marriage was sent to you, Darcy, and you came so soon after receiving it that I naturally assumed you cared for me. What changed your attitude, eh? Did you see someone else you fancied rather more than a half-man in a wheelchair? You will tell me——'

'There never was a proposal of marriage.' Darcy said frantically. 'The letter from your brother merely requested that I come on a visit to you. I was perfectly willing to do that, and it wasn't until I arrived that I was told I was expected to marry you. Your brother wouldn't accept a refusal. He said I owed you something for being the cause of the accident—he just wouldn't believe it wasn't altogether my fault. I truly meant to go through with the wedding, Ramon, but it wouldn't be fair on either of us. How could I make you happy if I didn't really love you——?'

'Who do you love?' His hands were grasping the arms of his chair until the knuckle bones seemed as if they'd break through his skin. 'Is it my big proud brother, with his fine body he can use so freely? Have you watched him riding and dancing—I could dance like that once upon a time, remember? I could arch a girl across my arm until her feet left the ground, and make love to English women any time I fancied. There was one, poor fool, who actually killed herself for love of me, and I was only a boy of seventeen at the time. How do you go for that, Darcy? I had it all, and then, you little bitch, you took it away from me!'

Darcy stared at him, her heart beating with such rapidity that it made her feel as if she might faint. She knew instantly that he referred to the governess who had ended her life in that bedroom upstairs. Ramon, a handsome, strutting youth of seventeen, amusing himself and satisfying his growing *machismo* by seducing a spinster a number of years older than himself.

And she had been ready to blame Julio! Darcy swayed and clutched at a nearby table edge; she felt suddenly sick and wanted to get away from Ramon. He had never needed her pity. He had been waiting behind a haggardly charming smile to become her husband so he could pay her back for the way he was. All along he had blamed her and made Julio believe that the accident had been caused by her faulty driving. Ramon didn't love her . . . he hated her.

Gathering her strength, she began to back away from him to the door, and deliberately his chair began to move, his jaw looking rigid as he got ready to propel the chair against her when she reached the door, where its wheels would slam against her legs and he'd be close enough to grab at her. She veered to one side and saw that the windows on to the patio outside were standing open. She sped towards them before Ramon could swing his wheelchair around. She fled outside, taking a deep breath of air and running as if pursued by a devil. That was surely what Ramon had turned into, the bitterness eating into him until all he lived for was to have his revenge on her.

All along it had been Ramon's *venganza*, planned to the very last detail, even that moment in the tack room when he had waited for Julio, holding a gun to his temple.

Suddenly, with shocking suddenness, Darcy ran into someone, crying out at the contact with a hard masculine shape.

'*Señorita*,' hands caught hold of her and steadied her, 'what on earth is wrong? What are you running away from?'

Darcy gazed up at the lean, dark, concerned face of Carlos, the young man who worked for Julio. 'I—oh, Carlos, will you take me to the railway station? I—I have to leave at once! Right away! Please, please do this for me!'

'But I don't understand, *señorita*.' He ran his gaze over her distressed face. 'What has happened to make you like this—you're trembling and frightened. If something or someone has frightened you, then the *dueño* must be told——'

'No!' She shook her head wildly. 'I have to get away, Carlos, as soon as possible, and I'd be so grateful if you'd take me to the station. I—I don't know the way, you see, and——'

He gripped her shoulders and shook his head. 'You have a fever, I can see it from the flush on your cheeks. You are still feeling the after-effects of the snakebite and are a little out of your head. Come, let me carry you into the house.' And he had swung her up into his arms before she could protest and was striding back in the direction of the patio from which she had fled. Darcy struggled against him, but his arms were too strong, and he was too pledged to Julio Valdez to do anything at all behind his back.

Darcy had to allow herself to be carried into the house and lowered into a deep chair. 'I'll fetch Doña Ansonia.' Carlos patted her hand like a concerned brother, and strode off in the direction of the little morning *sala* where Julio's aunt took breakfast and read her newspapers. Darcy shivered, her gaze fixed upon the doors that led into Ramon's apartment. She had vainly hoped never to set eyes on him again, but her escape from San Solito wasn't going to be so easy. How could it be? She had been a frightened fool to think she could run away. She was too deeply entangled in the lives of the Valdez men, trapped as if in the strands of their dark, complex personalities.

One of them she hopelessly loved ... the other one she feared. Despite his great good looks she had always felt an instinctive recoil from Ramon, and now she knew why. He was basically a sensualist and nothing more, but in Julio there were deep reserves of strength and duty and love of his land. Darcy felt a burning heat of tears at the back of her eyes and gathering in her throat ... she loved him so, and he was going to hate her when she had to tell him that she'd rejected Ramon and asked that the wedding be called off for ever.

CHAPTER TEN

DARCY tensed, staring helpless across the hall when the doors of Ramon's suite were flung open and he appeared clad in a ruffled shirt, dark pants, his hair well groomed above his lean face. Gomez was propelling his chair, but when he saw Darcy he said something to the attendant who with impassive politeness went off in the direction of the staff quarters.

Darcy could feel herself shrinking away as Ramon's chair came wheeling towards her.

'Ah, *buenos días, amigo.*' Julio came striding from beneath an archway, and in contrast to his brother he was wearing ivory-coloured pants and a black shirt. His hair wasn't quite so tidy, a black strand of it falling across his forehead, giving him a look that made Darcy feel weak.

'It's started to rain,' he said. 'I hope it won't be a downpour, not with the grapes coming on. We should have a bumper crop this year and I'm planning on a bigger yield of wine.'

'You and your wine!' Ramon gave a rather curt laugh. 'Is that all you think about, brother? When do you fit the women into your life? I presume you do take a fancy to a girl now and again?'

Julio drew his brows together and Darcy saw the tautening of his wide shoulders under the material

of his shirt. She knew at once what leapt into his mind
... had Dorina said something to Ramon after all?

'I don't mix work and pleasure,' he said. 'What's up
with you, Ramon? You look—odd.'

'Men in wheelchairs usually do, brother, to those
who can walk upright and dazzle the ladies with their
charms. I wonder how you'd feel, Julio, if you had to
sit in this damned thing? Quite frankly I don't think
you'd be able to stand it—ah, stand it! That's a laugh,
eh?'

'Ramon——' Julio took a step towards his brother,
his eyes glinting with concern. 'What is it, *amigo*? Why
are you speaking like this? Has someone upset you—
said something?'

'Oh yes.' Ramon flung out a hand in Darcy's direction. 'Ask her what she has said to me! No, I'll tell you,
brother! She has informed me that she doesn't wish
to marry a cripple—that she doesn't fancy being the
wife of a man whose lower half is useless. She wants
someone strong and strutting, who can make her sob
with passion and get her with child. Being married to
me would be no fun for her, and the proposal she
accepted with such alacrity she has now flung back in
my face.'

Ramon paused and fixed his eyes upon Julio, while
Darcy took a shaky breath, her eyes swimming with
tears which she tried to hold back by looking up at
the chandeliers that seemed to hang from the hall ceiling like enormous jewelled spiders.

'You brought her here, brother,' Ramon said deliberately, 'and now I'd be obliged if you'd tell her to go
to hell.'

An almost unearthly silence followed, broken suddenly by a deep and menacing growl of thunder. The
next instant lightning flickered across the hall and

they heard the rain beating at the stone pavement of
the patio outside.

'I cannot abide storms!' Dorina came running across
the hall in a tulip-coloured skirt and loose silk blouse.
She flung herself at Julio and drew his arm around her,
and almost like an automaton he permitted this for
several tense seconds, until suddenly he flung her to
one side. His nostrils were carved and distended and his
eyes were seething with a storm of his own.

'Is this true, what my brother tells me?' he demanded
of Darcy.

She nodded wordlessly. In essence Ramon's embel-
lishments were true enough. She wanted Julio ... his
passion ... his child ... but she knew from the look
of him that all she had right now was his furious anger
that she had broken with Ramon.

'What is going on?' Dorina stood there with her
hands on her hips, her bosom heaving under the
flowered silk of her blouse. She stared at Julio and then
swung her gaze to Ramon. A flash of comprehension
came into her eyes. 'So you know, eh? You are now wise
to what has been going on behind your back, Ramon?'

Ramon caught his breath. 'Dorina——?'

'These two!' She snapped her fingers, first at Darcy,
then at Julio. 'She has been sleeping with him—ask
him, go on! She has been getting from Julio what you
can't give her!'

'That isn't true!' Suddenly Darcy was upon her feet,
unable to bear any more of this in dumb and stricken
silence. 'Julio would never—never do anything to hurt
his brother. Last night I was feeling low and out of
courtesy and kindness Julio came and talked to me.
Nothing happened! He fell asleep, that's all—he fell
asleep in my bed because he was tired—because he
carries all the concerns and problems of this estate by

himself and has been doing so for a long time. Who really cares that sometimes the burden is a heavy one? You see only his strong body, but do any of you ever wonder if his spirit feels lonely and weary and in need of comfort? No matter what crops up, Julio can cope— Julio can manage—Julio can put things right!'

Darcy took a deep breath and faced Ramon. 'Julio tried his best to put things right for you, Ramon, so don't blame him in any way because I can't go through with our marriage. There has been nothing between your brother and me that you need worry about. From the very start he's had your welfare at heart. I know that your happiness comes before his own.'

'My happiness?' Ramon glared at her and thumped his legs. 'You were a damned shrinking violet from the word go, scared out of your wits to let a man put his hand on your leg. *Por Dios*, do you fondly imagine I ever wanted you here because I couldn't live without you? I wanted to have my own back and knowing what a sentimental little idiot you were—tears in your eyes when you listened to that old *hombre* singing *September Song*—I knew I could get you here, make you marry me and be my nursemaid until you staggered over your own feet and your eyes and hair lost their shine. I lived for that, and now——'

Abruptly he swung his chair forward, lunging it at her, but the side wheels skidded on the smooth tiles of the hall and the momentum overbalanced the wheel-chair and as it crashed on its side Ramon was thrown out of it, landing with a thud the instant Julio leapt to catch him and failed.

As Julio knelt to lift him, Ramon thrust him away, his right leg giving a jerk.

'He—he moved his leg,' Dorina cried out. 'Did you see—he moved!'

Ramon lay there panting while the thunder swept over the house and the lightning flared across their faces, struck as if by shock.

'My lamb—my poor Ramon, what has happened?' His chair lay on its side, the wheels spinning as Doña Ansonia came hastening across the hall to where Ramon had fallen.

Ramon and Julio were like images staring at each other, and then all at once they started to laugh. It was incredible to Darcy as their joint laughter rang out that they could find anything amusing in what had occurred.

'Your leg moved, *amigo*! Yes, it moved!' Julio shouted the words exultantly so they echoed to the high ceiling, and like a clap of thunder inside her Darcy understood what had happened ... the charge of emotion, the hot anger, the impulsive movement of the wheelchair which had flung him to the floor, had released the paralytic grip on Ramon's nervous system and he had at last shown a sign that he wasn't totally helpless.

A tremulous wave of thankfulness swept over Darcy. She stood a moment watching as Doña Ansonia fussed over Ramon, her ringed hands stroking his face. Julio was flexing his hands at the sides of his ivory pants, and when Dorina flung herself at him, he laughed again, looped an arm about her waist and brushed her forehead with his lips.

That seemed the signal for Darcy to go. She turned away, walking on tremulous legs to the staircase. She was truly the outsider now—now she could leave San Solito and no one would bother to detain her. As she took hold of the stair post she saw Carlos standing a little in shadow watching her.

'Will you take me to the station now, Carlos?' she asked.

He inclined his head. 'Any time you are ready, *señorita*. As soon as you have said goodbye——'

'No.' She shook her head. 'I couldn't face that. I'll get my things and meet you quietly round by the garage. I—I'd rather do it this way—you must understand?'

'I heard what was said,' he agreed. 'I saw what happened. The *dueño* will be none too pleased if you leave clandestinely. Out of politeness he would wish to say *adiós*.'

Darcy gave an uncontrollable shiver. She couldn't bear to face a polite and cool goodbye from Julio. She would leave while she still had control of her tears.

'Please, Carlos,' her eyes pleaded with him, 'take me quickly and quietly to the station. Don Julio won't be angry with you. He'll understand why I didn't stay to say *adiós*.'

'As you wish, *señorita*. I shall be waiting for you.'

'Thank you.' She hurried upstairs, feeling an ache in her ankle as she hastened along the gallery to her bedroom. Inside it was gloomy from the rain that was still coming down, driving against the windows and letting in steely flashes of lightning. A storm of the gods, she thought, as she dragged things from the wardrobe and drawers and bundled them into her hooped bag. She swung her coat around her and with equal carelessness bundled her hair into a knitted hat. She swept her toiletries into her handbag, glanced once around this room in which Julio had embraced her and then quickly left.

When she reached the stairs Darcy glanced down into the hall. It was empty now and the chair had been wheeled away. No doubt the family were in the *sala* having a glass of the Valdez wine in order to celebrate ... the signs looked good for Ramon, and perhaps in time, Darcy thought wistfully, Julio would forgive her for the truths she had had to bring into the open. At least they had worked wonders for Ramon. One day he would walk again and the bitterness would be gone from his eyes and they would be alive again with that old devilish sparkle. Maybe he would stay at San Solito to help Julio run the estate.

Darcy walked quickly past the doors of the *sala*, making her way out of a sideway that led in the direction of the garage. The rain had slowed down a little and she could smell the trees after their drenching and saw petals on the ground.

The big car was standing in the driveway and Carlos, clad in a white jacket, was at the wheel.

'Don't bother to get out,' she said, and slid in beside him, leaning over to place her baggage on the rear seat. She straightened and sat gazing ahead of her as the engine purred and the car slid smoothly along in the softer fall of rain. The wipers moved against the window, and Darcy fought to control her tears as the big Spanish house receded in the background. She daren't cry just yet, for once she started she wouldn't be able to stop. She blinked her lashes and her voice was husky when she said to the man at her side:

'It's very kind of you to do me this favour, and I feel certain the *dueño* will understand why I left in this informal way. He won't blame anyone but me.'

'He would blame himself, *carisima*, if he allowed you to leave him.'

Her heart lurched and with a cry that seemed to come from deep inside her she turned fully to look at

the man who was driving. Her eyes dwelt hungrily on
that slightly hollowed profile with the sideburn slashing down to the lean jaw. She took in his rain-mussed
hair, his brown throat in the opening of the black shirt
beneath the white jacket. Her gaze dropped to his
hands on the wheel, strong, long-fingered, the glint of
a carved gold ring on his left hand.

'Julio!'

'None other, my foolish child.' The car came to a
smooth halt and the next instant he was reaching for
her, his touch sending shock waves of delight and
wonder all the way through her. Through her lashes
she met his eyes and her mind had no control over her
body as he caught her to him and his lips closed hard
on hers, consuming her in a release of passion that
couldn't be contained or questioned at this moment.

Darcy was sure of nothing but the incredible wonder
and warmth of his mouth on hers ... so unlooked-for,
so unexpected, so deliriously needed. Her arms were
wrapped tightly around him, her fingers deep in his
black hair, her lips parted to his penetrating kisses. Her
bones seemed to be flowing with the hot mercury of
love, and if after this she wasn't to have him, then she'd
die. It would surely kill her if agony had to follow the
ecstasy.

Allowing her to catch her breath, he rested his
mouth against her warm throat. A pulsating oneness
held them quiet and softly panting for moments on end,
and then he took a deep rough breath.

'*El momento de verdad*,' he whispered. 'I adore you
to madness and thank God I have a friend who came
and told me to my face that a little English girl was
running away from my house with a crucified look in
her eyes. One of the reasons Carlos and I work well

together is that we have empathy, and I believe he guessed some time ago that I was desperately in love with my brother's *novia*.'

'But I——' She trembled. 'Julio, I can't—don't make me——'

'Sweet eyes,' he held her face in the frame of his hands, 'that is over, finished. I want you for myself.'

'But you were so angry with me, so furious that I told Ramon I couldn't marry him.' She scanned Julio's face for any lingering sign of that anger, but it was curiously gentle, the tawny eyes smouldering like the softest gold in his dark face. Her very bones ached with love of him, but did he truly love her?

'I believed Ramon was sincere about you, *lindisima*. Had I guessed the true nature of why he wanted you, then I'd have wrung his neck. By the gods, he had reason to be bitter, but not in that way, wanting you so he could wear all the soft, warm youth out of you.' Julio tenderly stroked a hand over her hair, brushing the deep soft wave from her eyes. He bent his head and kissed her eyes, moving his lips so he felt her lashes when she blinked them. He gazed down deeply into her eyes, deeper until with a gasp of shyness she clutched him around the neck and buried her face in his neck.

He wanted her, she could see that for herself, but love was something else ... love was everything, desire and beyond desire, when sometimes it was joy just to sit and hold hands while a fire burned softly in a quiet room.

'Julio,' she was breathing unsteadily, 'what you feel— is it just a physical thing? You said I aroused the— the animal in you.'

'You do,' he growled. 'Animal, protector, opponent —husband. I lust for you, and I love you at that same time, little one. That's the way of it, with a man and a woman. That's love, *adorada*. Come, don't I arouse the tigress in you?'

Beneath her fingernails she felt the smooth nape of his neck and gently she dug them into him. 'Beloved brute! You kissed Dorina! What of her?'

'She's a huntress, my love, and she'll survive, I assure you, to find for herself some other *dueño* who will allow her to rule his roost and look stunning for his guests.' Julio drew Darcy's face away from his neck, holding her ready for his threatening kiss. 'You are going to be my wife, my mistress, my children's sweet mother. You are going to be mine, now and always. Now kiss me and I'll teach you all about the *quemadero* of love.'

Darcy yielded her lips to the flame ... burning, exciting, like the desert, in her lover's eyes.

Poignant tales of love, conflict, romance and adventure

Harlequin Presents...

Elegant and sophisticated novels of
great romantic fiction . . .
12 all-time best-sellers.

Join the millions of avid Harlequin readers all over the world who delight in the magic of a really exciting novel.

From the library of Harlequin Presents all-time best-sellers we are proud and pleased to make available the 12 selections listed here.

Combining all the essential elements you expect of great storytelling, and bringing together your very favorite authors—you'll thrill to these exciting tales of love, conflict, romance, sophistication and adventure. You become involved with characters who are interesting, vibrant, and alive. Their individual conflicts, struggles, needs, and desires grip you, the reader, until the final page.

Have you missed any of these *Harlequin Presents*...

Offered to you in the sequence in which they were originally printed—this is an opportunity for you to add to your Harlequin Presents . . . library.

This elegant and sophisticated series was first introduced in 1973, and has been a huge success ever since. The world's top romantic fiction authors combine glamour, exotic locales and dramatic and poignant love themes woven into gripping and absorbing plots to create a unique reading experience in each novel.

You'd expect to pay $1.75 or more for this calibre of best-selling novel. At only **$1.25 each,** Harlequin Presents are truly top value, top quality entertainment.

Don't delay—order yours today